The
Ultimate
Wedding & Ceremony Workbook

For The
'Planning-Impaired'

Rev. Amy E. Long

Apex Publications
P.O. Box 2166
Elk Grove, CA 95759

For information, contact Apex Publications, P.O. Box 2166 Elk Grove, CA 95759, (916) 422-8687.

www.ministersupplies.com or Spiritual1@aol.com.

Edited by Stephanie A. Smith.
Cover Design by Monica Rothenbaum

ISBN 0-9664992-3-9

10 9 8 7 6 5 4 3 2 1

Acknowledgments:
    Some of the ceremonies included in this book have been modeled after, quoted from (Bible), or inspired by words found from a variety of sources. With that said, I would like to acknowledge the following persons, entities or things for their help: The Church of Divine Man, Rev. Stephanie Smith, the King James version of the Bible, Kahlil Gibran, and the Apache Indians.

For Aaron, who has always supported me in my crazy endeavors.

For Jessica, my favorite daughter and little bit of sunshine.

Also, to Connor, whom I love more than I can say.

Table Of Contents

How To Use This Book

1.   **Please Write In It!**

2.   Read the articles, and think lovingly and longingly about your perfect wedding day.

3.   Find all the '*Decisions to Make*' pages, mark them with a highlighter pen. Then, when you're ready, go back and answer the questions. Cross out what doesn't apply. This will help you make most, if not all, of the decisions about your wedding.

4.   Read through the ceremonies in the Appendix at the back of the book and choose what you like. Tear those out; arrange the ceremony how you want it, then put it aside to give to the minister (officiant) when you meet to talk about your wedding. (If you're afraid of losing it, you can use the '*Order of Ceremony*' page to fill in which parts you want, then tear it out later.)

5.   Find the '*Things to Acquire*' pages. Highlight these with a different color pen. When you're ready, go back and check off what you need, cross out what you won't need, fill in anything I've missed, and tear out the pages to take with you when you go shopping.

6.   Review the '*Day of Details*' pages and mark these with a third color pen. On the big day, tear them out to give to your wedding helper.

7.   Most importantly, *use* this book and allow yourself to relax a little.

Fairy Tale On A Budget

The hard part is done. You've found the perfect mate, the big question has been popped and the proposal has been accepted. You're getting married! That's great! Now that the shock has worn off, it's time to get down to making plans.

You've been dreaming of this day for years and you want it to be absolutely perfect. I understand. It'll probably go something like this: On that memorable day, servants will work for hours decorating the huge hall, preparing mountains of delicious food and making sure there is champagne on every table. You float in, garbed in miles of satin, rhinestones and sequins to the sound of a harp and violinist. After a perfect ceremony, your valet brings your carriage, pulled by six cute little mice who've been turned into Arabian horses just for that day. Ah, yes, that's how it shall be.

There's only one problem: The check to cover it all would bounce all the way to the bank. Sigh. What's the alternative then? A quick trip to the justice of the peace before riding off into the sunset on your moped?

It doesn't have to be that way. If money is an issue (and it usually is for the person parting with it), then read on. I have some of the most amazing suggestions for helping you to create an intimate, memorable, dazzling wedding for as many people as you can get to come. All this for the amazing low price of however much is in your budget. It really depends on how much work you want to do and how much time you give yourself to do it.

I'd suggest going to some local bridal shows. These are places where wedding professionals gather and give you the opportunity to check them out. This can be one stop shopping, which can save you oodles of time. They also often offer bridal show specials, which can save you money as well.

After you finish reading the articles in each section, spend some time going through the 'questions' checklist. Put a big fat line through anything that doesn't relate to you and make notes by the things that do. This way, you won't have to worry about forgetting something because the questions are all there. Immediately following the list of *Decisions*

To Make' is a list of *'Things To Acquire'*. Again, cross off what you don't need or highlight what you do and then, GO SHOPPING!

Back to the big event itself. Using the time-honored 'planning-impaired' technique, let's start in the middle someplace and work our way out. After the budget has been set, one of the next most important things to think about is *where* the ceremony itself will take place. There are many options available.

Perhaps, your budget is small, but your vision is large. A ceremony at a park might be just the answer. Or maybe your budget is really large, but you'd prefer something intimate so you can spend more money on your honeymoon. A backyard wedding may be perfect for you. However, if you don't have a friend with a backyard large enough to accommodate the number of guests you'd like to invite, you will probably want to rent a hall. Most privately-owned halls are extremely expensive to rent. However, there are some privately-owned halls that are merely *very* expensive to rent. Go with your budget on this one. You can often get deals on places when you attend any local Bridal Shows. One way to get around the high cost is to look into halls owned by the Park and Recreation department, VFW Halls, a community center, or other government-owned buildings. Some rooms are as low as $30 per hour.

The important thing when selecting a wedding site is that you choose one, which is a reflection of *who you are* as a couple. Casual or formal, upscale or down to earth. The site can be by a lake with a few close friends who are casually dressed, or a formal wedding in a church or posh hotel. As long as you feel comfortable there, it's the right place.

There are many ways to make whatever space you choose more personal; a favorite tablecloth on the candle/wine table or your favorite flowers set around the altar. The spot might be the place where you two first kissed (although on the stoop of your front door might be a little crowded). Or maybe the perfect place has the view of a beautiful lake that sparkles like the gleam in your beloved's eyes. (Okay, it's corny, but what's the harm in that?)

Go where you can have your friends and loved ones around you. Make it a comfortable place where you can laugh and smile and remember the joyous reason you're going to all this trouble in the first place.

Secrets To A Smoother Wedding Day

One of the most essential secrets to having your wedding day go more smoothly is to *Delegate, Delegate, Delegate!* What this means is that you get to relinquish control and put someone else in charge of the day-of details.

There are pages throughout the book that are designed as check-off lists for the day of the event. This includes topics such as: ceremony day-of details, emergency kit for wedding day, wedding photo list, & wedding helper check-off list for reception day-of details. Tear these out. Give them to a trusted and efficient friend or to your wedding coordinator.

It will be *her* job to make sure all of the boxes are checked, the lines drawn, the 'I-s' dotted, etc. It will be *your* job to let her do it.

> # *Delegate, Delegate, Delegate!*

There's nothing sadder than seeing a freaked out bride on her wedding day trying to get everything set up, organized and solved from the confines of the bride's dressing room. Better to just trust that someone else can handle it.

For yourself, the morning of the big day, go out to breakfast with your mom and/or your bridesmaids. Depending on what you have time for, consider getting a massage or sitting in a hot tub. Pamper yourself on this day of days like you never have before. After all, it's not every day that you get married; make the most of it!

The most important thing to remember on this special day, that no matter what else happens, you're doing what you set out to do -- marry the person you love most in the whole world. So, if the flower girl throws up, the groom passes out, the photographer doesn't show up or you break a nail, try to think of it as something that may seem like a problem now, but will make a great story to tell your kids later!

Personalizing Your Wedding Day

Unless your wedding is catered at a hotel, chances are you'll need to do some chair moving. This is a great opportunity for you to include your guests. The person assigned to taking care of tasks can ask people if they would help move a few chairs when needed. **People love to help**. You could also ask them to help by putting out some food or making punch. You may find that these same people will stay to help clean up as well. By inviting them to help on some small tasks, it makes them feel like they are part of the wedding. **Everybody likes to feel included**.

If you decide that catering the event is a little out of your price range, then ask a few close friends or relatives, who are itching to share in your excitement, if they would be so kind as to bring a food dish enough for, say, ten people. (This may change depending on how many people you've invited.) This can be their wedding gift to you. Hors d'oeuvres are a good idea. They're simple, easy to make, and can be more interesting than catered food (although, if you can afford it, a good caterer is worth his/her weight in gold).

If you're concerned that the whole thing will look mishmash, you can transfer the food onto inexpensive matching trays. These can be bought at places that sell party supplies. A simpler plan can be to just place matching napkins under each dish or matching bows taped to the front of each dish.

One more thing -- the toast. Traditionally, only the best man and the fathers give a toast, but this is unrealistic. If given the chance, there are many people who would love to wish you well on your special day. Give them that chance. Pass the remote microphone (or talking stick, or whatever) and bask in the love.

A Question Of Etiquette

Sometimes the word 'etiquette' makes people feel a little uncomfortable. Their response is that, "etiquette is stuffy", "our wedding is casual" or "it's not really important." Well, the truth of the matter is, that response comes from people who aren't terribly sure what proper etiquette entails. That's the joy of etiquette. It tells you what to do when you're unsure. I'm going to mention a few little things about wedding etiquette and tradition.

As for seating, those best known to the bride sit on the left, as you walk down the aisle, and those best known to the groom sit on the right. The immediate family of the couple sits in the front rows. Make sure they know this. Guests usually wait for ushers to seat them. Ushers may or may not be wearing tuxedos, but a boutonniere is a nice consideration.

The mothers of the couple are usually seated as part of the processional. The father of the groom can walk on the other side of the mother of the groom or, if he prefers, can be already seated when the processional begins.

Traditionally, the groom first sees his bride's gown when she's walking down the aisle to greet him. When the bride arrives at her destination, it's customary for the bride to kiss her father's cheek (or whoever walked her down) and for the groom to shake his hand. This lets everyone know that it's an amicable event.

> **Please send thank-you notes.**

The **best man** is in charge of all sorts of things. **It is he who is in charge of issuing payment to the wedding professionals**. This can be prepared by enclosing the money in an envelope ahead of time and writing the names on the outside. The best man also may keep track of the license and steady the nerves of the groom. He carries the bride's ring, signs the marriage license, is usually the one who throws the groom his bachelor party and is occasionally in charge of seeing that the place is cleaned up afterwards.

The **maid of honor** helps the bride get ready, holds her flowers during the ceremony, carries the groom's ring, signs the marriage certificate and adjusts the bride's train or veil during the ceremony as needed. She also often is the one to throw the bridal shower (or bachelorette party). During the shower, it is customary for her to keep some of the bows and ribbons from the gifts and transform them into a mock bouquet to be used at the wedding rehearsal (if you decide to have one).

The **minister** is responsible for performing the ceremony, getting the requisite signatures, posing for a picture with the newlyweds and mailing the license in the envelope provided if the appropriate check for the court is enclosed. (It's about $16 for a certified copy of your license.) It's also good etiquette to specifically invite the minister to the reception. Later, send the minister a thank you card and a posed picture from the wedding.

Another quick topic I'd like to talk about is Registering. It used to be that one Registered at the large, well-known department stores for expensive place settings and silver. This is still certainly acceptable, but you may find that you don't get much of what you ask for unless your friends all have a fair amount of disposable income to spend on you. Nowadays, there are Registries for just about anyplace.

The next thing to decide is how to let people **know** where you're Registered. In more genteel times, people knew to ask the Mother of the Bride where her daughter was Registered. This is still the right thing to do, but most people don't know that. For Brides, it has become moderately acceptable to put Registry cards into the envelope with the invitation. It's still a little tacky, but how else to let people know? Even if you don't think you'll use them, be sure to ask for cards to put in with the invitations, just in case.

Let's spend a few moments talking about thank-you notes. These are so very important when it comes to weddings. You will get practice doing these after your bridal shower and again when all the gifts arrive. **Please send thank-you notes**. It's really that simple. They don't have to be long-winded, expensive things, as long as they are sent.

You can write them on cute little cards that have your new married name on them or you can pick some up at the local drugstore. The important thing is that they are sent within two months of the wedding (one month is really preferred) and that they specifically mention the item you received. If you're not sure what it is, then try and describe it or what you might use it for. If it is artwork, make a note that it looks nice on the mantel.

If you are given money, mention what you'll use it for, rather than the amount. "Thanks for the hundred bucks" doesn't sound as nice as, "We really appreciated your generous gift. We're going to use it to treat ourselves to dinner and a movie." Even if you're going to use it on bills, tell them you're going to save it for something special. People don't like to think of their wedding gift as being used to pay the electric bill.

Another thought about gifts: What if the gift you got is absolutely hideous? What if it's the third waffle maker or zillionth toaster? Do you ask them where they got it or if they could please send you the receipt? Hardly. The best plan is to behave as if it's the most stupendous gift in the world, then quietly exchange it at your earliest convenience. If asked, just reiterate how much you appreciated it. Chances are, nobody will ask.

Tipping: Many people are unsure about that. Generally speaking, if your minister, DJ, cake-person or caterer does a really good job, a tip is appreciated. Nobody will be offended. A tip is not expected, but if someone goes that extra mile for you and helps make your day extra special, it's a great way to show your appreciation.

Ooooh, one last thing. It's best to leave the present-opening until **after** the honeymoon. (Only at birthday parties do you open them right there). The reason for this is two-fold: It takes a long time to open presents, record who gave what and to keep them all together **and** what if you get something hideous, two or three of one thing or something that you don't even know what it is? Very awkward. It's a good idea to put a trusted friend or family member in charge of taking the wedding gifts to your home or theirs until you return from your honeymoon. You might consider having a little get-together with a few close friends and family who would love to watch you open your wedding gifts. This might also be a good time to eat the top layer of your cake. The tradition is to freeze it until your first anniversary, but it often doesn't freeze well (tastes yucky). You also will have to lug it around for a year (if you move) taking up valuable freezer space. If you do plan to eat it when you get back from your honeymoon, be sure the guardian of the cake knows to keep it refrigerated. Whipped cream toppings will get moldy after a week.

Some bakers have a deal that on your one-year anniversary, they will bake you an extra little cake for two. This is a nice touch because then you get a fresh cake with no hassle. The charge for this varies with each bakery.

A Theme By Any Other Name. . .

Some people might think that a wedding already has a theme; you're getting married. This is true. However, having another theme can help make the decorations easier to devise and can also help give the event an attitude, a specific feeling, a tone, so to speak.

The type of wedding you can have is as vast as your imagination. If you strongly identify with a certain ethnicity, then use that. Have Hula dancers, Tap dancers, Mexican dancers, Highland dancers, Mariachi bands, etc. Get creative. Have fun with it.

One example of an ethnic theme that I personally like, is an Irish/Scottish theme. A bagpiper can be found in the yellow pages or through any Irish or Scottish organizations (found in the phone book under, 'Social Organizations'). They may also be able to direct you to a Highland Dance troupe to perform while you're out taking bridal pictures. If you want to go all out, the bridal party (or just the groom) can each wear a kilt. If your groom fears the idea of flashing his knobby knees to the crowd, then perhaps a plaid tie and cummerbund.

The type of wedding you can have is as vast as your imagination.

You may consider a carnival theme. You can hire a clown to entertain while you're out taking wedding pictures. There can be some carnival-type games, like ping pong balls thrown in fish bowls, bean bag toss, popcorn in little bags, etc. If you make it seem like a circus wedding, you can have the ceremony be the main attraction in the center ring.

Another theme is Mardi Gras. For decorations, you can get some of those masks that just cover the eyes and are secured by a rubber band or ones held in front of the face by a stick. At a party supply store, you can find lots of the little plastic toys along with some chocolate coins. Maybe even a piñata, to continue the party feel.

Perhaps you are interested in a Renaissance wedding. Held outside, guests may come dressed in costume, as well as the minister and other wedding professionals. Hire a psychic to tell fortunes and maybe a wandering minstrel. The DJ can play appropriate music, or you can hire a two- or three-piece band to soothe your guests. The music department of your local college might furnish the musicians for little or no cost.

A balloon-style wedding is a great way to decorate. Balloons can fill the ceiling, be used on the tables as centerpieces, line the aisle where the bride will walk, and left free standing around the room, with the ribbon weighted down by a decorated brick or soda can. Helium in disposable containers may be purchased at party supply stores. You can also purchase colored sticks and plastic holders to put the balloons on. This enables you to blow them up by hand and costs much less than the helium. A bouquet of three or more makes a nice table decoration.

A Christmas wedding is easy because you can put the presents under your Christmas tree and use it as a center focus. The decorations for Christmas are festive and are something that most people already have, so it can save you money.

Along the same lines is having a costume wedding. It can, perhaps, be a country wedding, complete with square/line dancing (whatever you prefer), sawdust on the floor and peanuts on the tables. You can even hire professional square dancers to entertain. Other costumes can be of the Halloween variety or anything else that strikes your fancy.

If you wish to go a simpler route, how about a garden style or rose garden wedding? Held outside, fresh flowers on the tables, bridesmaids dressed in flower-print dresses and perhaps a harpist or flutist providing the music. The bouquet could be a simple bunch of daisies.

It has become rather popular to burn some CDs of the couple's favorite songs as favors, with the couple's picture on the front, but I believe that infringes on existing copyrights.

I've seen favors provided that were individual squares of pretty tile with the bride and groom's names and wedding date on the back. The tiles could later be used to protect your countertop when you set down a hot dish. They're inexpensive, simple and useful. As a plus, your friends and family will be much more likely to remember you anniversary!

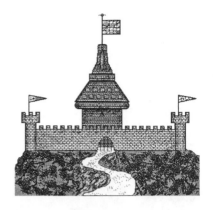

Wedding Date_____
Size of Wedding_____
Amount of Budget_____
Wedding Colors Chosen_____
Theme of Wedding_____

I. Decisions to Make: Location

A. Before you start looking:

_____At someone's home?
_____In a church?
_____Renting a hall?
_____Day of week preferred?
_____Ceremony: Inside, outside or either?
_____Reception: Inside, outside or either?
_____Weather expectations? (warm, hot, cold, rainy, etc.)
_____Do you want liquor at the wedding?
_____Is liquor allowed/extra expense for deposit or guard?
_____How many tables will you need?
_____How many chairs will you need?
_____Do you want the reception catered?

B. When you have a place in mind:

List the different facilities below, then use the numbered lines to keep track of the various bits of information.

1._____ Phone_____Contact_____
2._____ Phone_____Contact_____
3._____ Phone_____Contact_____
4._____ Phone_____Contact_____

_____
_____

Number each facility you call and put the answers here.

1	2	3	4	
1____	2____	3____	4____	Cost
1____	2____	3____	4____	How many guests will it hold?
1____	2____	3____	4____	Deposit required?
1____	2____	3____	4____	Day of week available?
1____	2____	3____	4____	Discounts for Sundays?
1____	2____	3____	4____	Is it available for rehearsal?
1____	2____	3____	4____	For how many hours is it available?
1____	2____	3____	4____	Rehearsal Charge?
1____	2____	3____	4____	Who will open facility?
1____	2____	3____	4____	How soon before ceremony can you get in?
1____	2____	3____	4____	Is there a number to call if facility not opened?_____
1____	2____	3____	4____	Liquor Allowed?
1____	2____	3____	4____	Liquor License needed?
1____	2____	3____	4____	Guard required?
1____	2____	3____	4____	Aisle on grass or hard surface? (consider sinking heels)
1____	2____	3____	4____	If held inside: Air-Conditioned/heated?
1____	2____	3____	4____	Is there enough convenient parking?
1____	2____	3____	4____	Bathrooms close by?
1____	2____	3____	4____	Do bathrooms need decorating?
1____	2____	3____	4____	Changing area available for bride?
1____	2____	3____	4____	Mirror available in changing room?
1____	2____	3____	4____	Enough room for bride's attendants?
1____	2____	3____	4____	Changing area available for groom?
1____	2____	3____	4____	Enough room for groom's attendants?
1____	2____	3____	4____	Are chairs provided?
1____	2____	3____	4____	Are tables provided?
1____	2____	3____	4____	Will facility set them up?
1____	2____	3____	4____	Space for seating guests?
1____	2____	3____	4____	Room for dancing?
1____	2____	3____	4____	Separate chair arrangement for eating?
1____	2____	3____	4____	Must you use their caterer?
1____	2____	3____	4____	Kitchen available?
1____	2____	3____	4____	Cooking privileges?
1____	2____	3____	4____	Microwave?
1____	2____	3____	4____	Fridge provided?
1____	2____	3____	4____	Extra coolers needed?
1____	2____	3____	4____	Freezer to store ice?
1____	2____	3____	4____	Can you tape/tack things on the walls?

II. Things To Acquire: Ceremony Site

(If Not Applicable, Cross Out)

Altar Area:
_____ Platform
_____ Podium for minister
_____ Microphone for minister
_____ Gazebo
_____ Archway
_____ Aisle runner (colored?)
_____ Table for wine/candle ceremony
_____ Tablecloth
_____ One big candle (for candle-lighting)
_____ Two tapered candles (for candle-lighting)
_____ Matches/lighter (for candles)
_____ Wine goblet (wine ceremony)
_____ Liquid to put in goblet
_____ Ribbons (ribbon ceremony)
_____ Flowers by altar
_____ Masking tape or duct tape (to hold down aisle runner)

Other things needed for ceremony:
_____ Ring bearer pillow
_____ Rings
_____ Rose petals for flower girl(s)
_____ Rose petal basket for flower girl(s)
_____ Video Camera(s)
_____ Processional Music (disc jockey would have)
_____ Bridal March (disc jockey should provide)
_____ Recessional Music (disc jockey would have)
_____ Wedding license
_____ Guest Book/Pen
_____ Doves to release
_____ Butterflies to release
_____ Emotions to release

_____ _____
_____ _____

III. Ceremony Day-Of Details

(Give to assigned person to delegate tasks)

Bridal party:

_____ All pre-ceremony pictures taken?
_____ Bride ready to go?
_____ Does Bride have cloth handkerchief?
_____ Maid/Matron of honor have Groom's ring?
_____ Corsages on?
_____ Bridal party has bouquets?

Groom party:

_____ Groom ready to go?
_____ Does Groom have cloth handkerchief?
_____ Boutonnieres on?
_____ Best Man have Bride's ring? (if no ring-bearer)
_____ Groom and groomsmen in their places?

Ceremony site:

_____ Aisle runner down?
_____ Flowers at altar?
_____ Candles put out for ceremony?
_____ Wax pre-lit off the wick?
_____ Wine goblet out?
_____ Goblet filled and ready to go?

Other ceremony considerations:

_____ Minister ready?
_____ Do children have their ribbons (for ceremony?)
_____ Flower girls have their petals ready?
_____ Ring bearer have rings (or just pillow)?
_____ Parents of little ones waiting in front rows to collect child?
_____ Does disc jockey have processional and recessional music?
_____ Parents of couple know their part (if any)?
_____ Wedding license available for signing?
_____ Video cameras set up for best shots? (not their backs!)
_____ Is minister's microphone hooked up?
_____ Is someone assigned to pay wedding professionals?

IV. Emergency Kit For Wedding Day

_____ Extra bobby pins
_____ Safety pins
_____ Duct tape/masking tape
_____ Matches
_____ Hair spray
_____ Lipstick
_____ Nail polish (for touch-ups)
_____ Comb/Brush
_____ Bottled Water for Bride and Groom.
_____ Healthy Snacks for Bride and Groom (you don't want to get sick).
_____ Another set of jewelry (necklace, earrings, etc.)
_____ Extra cloth handkerchiefs
_____ Smelling salts (if Groom seems unusually nervous)
_____ Brown bag (for hyperventilating)
_____ Pepto Bismol/Antacids, etc.
_____ Scissors
_____ 'Shout' wipes – they'll get out just about any stain.
_____ Extra tape of processional and recessional music
_____ Copy of ceremony
_____ Extra video tape (if friend is taping it)
_____ Extra film for camera (you can't have too many pictures!)
_____ Any medications you usually take.
_____ Barf bag (hey, you can't be too prepared!)

_____ _____

_____ _____

_____ _____

V. Wedding Day 'Who's Who'

The Wedding Party: Who will be:	Name	Phone #
Maid of honor		
Matron of honor		
Bridesmaid		
Bridesmaid		
Bridesmaid		
Bridesmaid		
Bridesmaid		
Bridesmaid		
Best man		
Groomsman		
Groomsman		
Groomsman		
Groomsman		
Groomsman		
Groomsman		
Flower girl		
Flower girl		
Flower girl		
Ring bearer		
Usher		
Usher		
Usher		
Usher		
Wedding coordinator		
Minister (Officiant)		
Vocalist		
Musicians		
Disc Jockey		
Photographer		
Videographer		

To Rehearse or Not To Rehearse. . .

Whether or not you need a formal rehearsal really depends on the complexity of your wedding and fragility of your nerves.

Rehearsals do serve a very important purpose. They give the whole party a chance to get together in one place and spend a little time talking about what's happening. It also gives you a chance for a dry run. This is important if the walk to the altar is going to be unusual, there are lots of attendants and flower girls/ring bearers, or you're really nervous and want to make sure everything is going to be just perfect.

If you decide to rehearse, you'll have to find out if the church or hall will let you in to practice and for how long. (There may be an extra charge for this.) If not possible, you may need to make-do practicing elsewhere. You also may need to decide whether you need the minister there or not. Some ministers charge extra for the service. Wedding coordinators offer rates for day-of service, which may include the rehearsal. If you don't have a coordinator and are nervous about who walks whom, use the Processional Sheet (on page 29) to help you. A 'take charge' friend of yours would probably love to be asked to help direct.

Another thing to think about is the rehearsal dinner. This is usually paid for by the groom's family. If this is not an option, consider keeping it really simple and ordering several large pizzas for everyone. This may work out best for some people because it has the added advantage of helping everyone to keep casual and informal for the rehearsal. **Whatever you can do to keep the stress to a minimum is worth it.**

During the rehearsal dinner is also a time that you may give your attendants and groomsmen token gifts to show your appreciation for their involvement on your special day. A heartfelt token is more valuable here than an expensive gift.

Oh, it's also a nice gesture to invite to dinner any wedding professionals who you want to attend the rehearsal. They may not come, but it's nice to ask.

VI. Decisions to Make: Rehearsal

_____Are you having a rehearsal?

_____Do you need the minister there?

_____Decide about processional (see page 29)

_____Are you having a rehearsal dinner?

_____Are you going out to dinner?

_____Will you need to make reservations?

_____Ordering pizza, etc.?

_____When will the hall let you in to practice?

_____For how long can you practice there?

_____Is there an extra charge for this?

_____Cheaper to do it all in one day?

_____Where will you hold practice?

_____Have you put someone in charge to coordinate?

_____Are you having a Wedding Coordinator?

_____Gifts for Maid of Honor/Best Man?

_____Gifts for Attendants?

Things To Acquire

_____Gift for Maid of Honor

_____Gift for Best Man

_____Gifts for Attendants

_____Gifts for Groomsmen

_____Reservations at a restaurant

_____Pizza for dinner

_____Place to rehearse

In Search Of . . . Clergy

It used to be, in generations gone by, that everybody had a local religious leader (minister, priest, rabbi, whomever) who could be counted on to provide the best in local services. That's not true so much now. And there is no need to apologize! Even for those who may have a favorite, that person may not conduct ceremonies, may not always be available to perform a ceremony when needed or perhaps you are from different backgrounds and can't decide. So, the search is on.

It may seem strange, but one of the easiest ways to find a minister (or rabbi, etc.) is through the yellow pages. They are most likely listed under *Wedding Supplies and Services*, but can also be found under *Clergy.* The former is the best place to find non-denominational ministers. There are also many large websites which cater to brides. www.theknot.com is one that is national.

One of the most important considerations when finding a minister (officiant) is that you feel comfortable with that person. You like the way he/she talks, the way he/she carries him/herself and his/her attitude in general. During one of the most stressful days of your life, you'll want a minister who can put you at ease.

You might also inquire if he/she would be willing to perform a ceremony that you have chosen (from the Appendix, for example). Some ministers (officiants) are very strict about such things and will only do a traditional ceremony or one written themselves. Most, however, are far more flexible.

It's customary to meet with the minister ahead of time to choose or discuss the ceremony. If you have chosen a ceremony already from this book, you can take the time to review it with the minister as well as clear up any questions. It's also nice to see some pictures from that minister's previous weddings. Although some ministers wear a black robe for ceremonies, many don't. You certainly don't want your minister to clash with your wedding colors!

Many ministers will go to the rehearsal as part of the package, whereas others will charge an extra fee. If the latter is the case, save your money. Included on page 29 are sample processionals you can choose from. It's easier than you think. You'll do great. Relax.

VII. Decisions To Make:

Minister/Ceremony

The Minister (Officiant):

_____Minister (officiant) from your church?

_____Found in Yellow Pages/Bridal Shows/Referral?

_____Minister's experience?

_____Counseling required?

_____Charge for consultation?

_____Minister invited to reception?

The Service Itself:

_____Time of ceremony?

_____Non-Denominational ceremony?

_____Religious or non-religious preferred?

_____Do you want to choose entire ceremony yourself?

_____Writing own vows?

_____Couple want your backs to guests or to face each other?

_____Your children involved in ceremony?

_____Candle ceremony?

_____Wine ceremony?

_____Family ceremony?

_____Who will walk the bride down the aisle?

_____Anyone doing a reading?

_____Anyone singing a song?

_____Do you want a ring bearer?

_____Do you want flower girls?

_____How many?

_____How many attendants?

_____Will you need help with the processional? (see next page)

_____Microphone available for ceremony?

_____Guest seating anywhere or assigned?

_____Special seating for handicapped/elderly?

VIII. Processional Examples

The following are examples of different processionals. There are no hard and fast rules about how it should be done. Generally, the Bride's family is on the left facing the minister and the Groom's family is on the right. Read through and you'll get the idea. (Front rows should be reserved for family members.) The flower girl always goes right before the bride.

Example 1
Groom, Best Man, and Groomsmen start at altar (on the right)
Mother of the Bride seated by Usher
Mother of the Groom seated by Usher
Bridesmaids walking alone
Maid of Honor walking alone
Flower Girl/Ring Bearer
Bride

Example 2
Best Man seats Mother of the Bride (stands by altar)
Groom seats Mother of the Groom (stands by altar)
Ring Bearer
Maid of Honor walks alone
Flower Girl
Bride

Example 3
Groom waits at the altar
Mother of the Bride seated by Usher
Mother of the Groom seated by Usher
Groomsmen each walk down with a Bridesmaid
Best Man walks Maid of Honor
Flower Girl/Ring Bearer
Bride

Example 4
Best Man seats Mother of the Bride
Groom seats Mother of the Groom (waits at altar)
Best Man has meanwhile walked back around (not up the aisle)
Groomsmen walk Bridesmaids
Ring bearer
Best Man walks down Maid of Honor
Flower Girl
Bride

When Is The Right Time

In many wedding planners, there is included an extremely important timeline for getting all of your planning done. I, however, don't have one of those. I don't think they work. Why? Because it's all so relative and all so personal.

There are some people who like to think fast, plan fast and do everything at lightening speed. I've seen some people plan beautiful weddings in about a month. Other people like to take their time, consider every angle and just leisurely move through the process. Both types are going about it totally right. This is the good news and why I don't think the precise timelines work.

When planning your wedding, use your common sense. Are you getting married in a well-known facility in June on a Saturday afternoon? If so, then you'd better start reserving things a year ahead of time to secure everything. If you want it in the timeframe of November through February, and are considering a Sunday, then you've got a little more time.

Think about availability. It's easier to secure wedding professionals and ceremony/reception sites on Fridays or Sundays. It's also possible that you'll get a better rate for the cost of the site on those days as well. This is especially true if you book your wedding at an off time. Weddings don't happen as often in November through about January or February. Ask for a discount if you're doing it at a slow time.

For your honeymoon, this is also true of Bed and Breakfast Inns. Their off-seasons rates are substantially lower, as are their midweek rates. So, if you marry on a Sunday, then you'll save money all the way around.

The only time where off-season planning could cost you more might be the flowers. If you want roses out of season, then you're going to pay through the nose for them. A solution could be to either use silk flowers or find something in season. Your local florist may be able to suggest something.

My guess is that this imperative, absolute, rigid timeline thing was written more for the wedding professionals than for the brides. They like to book their work far in advance so they can plan their lives. This is understandable, but it's also not your problem. Move at your own pace and plan it at your leisure. The phone book is *full* of wedding professionals and ceremony sites to serve you.

IX. The Quest For Wedding Professionals

Minister

Name_____Phone#_____Cost_____Available?____
Name_____Phone#_____Cost_____Available?____
Name_____Phone#_____Cost_____Available?____
Name_____Phone#_____Cost_____Available?____

Disc Jockey

Name_____Phone#_____Cost_____Available?____
Name_____Phone#_____Cost_____Available?____
Name_____Phone#_____Cost_____Available?____
Name_____Phone#_____Cost_____Available?____

Photographer

Name_____Phone#_____Cost_____Available?____
Name_____Phone#_____Cost_____Available?____
Name_____Phone#_____Cost_____Available?____
Name_____Phone#_____Cost_____Available?____

Videographer

Name_____Phone#_____Cost_____Available?____
Name_____Phone#_____Cost_____Available?____
Name_____Phone#_____Cost_____Available?____
Name_____Phone#_____Cost_____Available?____

Caterer

Name_____Phone#_____Cost_____Available?____
Name_____Phone#_____Cost_____Available?____
Name_____Phone#_____Cost_____Available?____
Name_____Phone#_____Cost_____Available?____

Baker (for cake - may be the same as caterer)

Name_____Phone#_____Cost_____Available?____
Name_____Phone#_____Cost_____Available?____
Name_____Phone#_____Cost_____Available?____
Name_____Phone#_____Cost_____Available?____

Limousine Service
Name_____Phone#_____Cost_____Available?____
Name_____Phone#_____Cost_____Available?____
Name_____Phone#_____Cost_____Available?____
Name_____Phone#_____Cost_____Available?____

Wedding Coordinator
Name_____Phone#_____Cost_____Available?____
Name_____Phone#_____Cost_____Available?____
Name_____Phone#_____Cost_____Available?____
Name_____Phone#_____Cost_____Available?____

Ice-Carver
Name_____Phone#_____Cost_____Available?____
Name_____Phone#_____Cost_____Available?____
Name_____Phone#_____Cost_____Available?____
Name_____Phone#_____Cost_____Available?____

Dove/Butterfly Release Operator
Name_____Phone#_____Cost_____Available?____
Name_____Phone#_____Cost_____Available?____
Name_____Phone#_____Cost_____Available?____
Name_____Phone#_____Cost_____Available?____

Vocalist
Name_____Phone#_____Cost_____Available?____
Name_____Phone#_____Cost_____Available?____
Name_____Phone#_____Cost_____Available?____
Name_____Phone#_____Cost_____Available?____

Dancers
Name_____Phone#_____Cost_____Available?____
Name_____Phone#_____Cost_____Available?____
Name_____Phone#_____Cost_____Available?____
Name_____Phone#_____Cost_____Available?____

Other Entertainment
Name_____Phone#_____Cost_____Available?____
Name_____Phone#_____Cost_____Available?____
Name_____Phone#_____Cost_____Available?____
Name_____Phone#_____Cost_____Available?____

Bagpiper
Name_____Phone#_____Cost_____Available?____
Name_____Phone#_____Cost_____Available?____
Name_____Phone#_____Cost_____Available?____
Name_____Phone#_____Cost_____Available?____

Musicians
Name_____Phone#_____Cost_____Available?____
Name_____Phone#_____Cost_____Available?____
Name_____Phone#_____Cost_____Available?____
Name_____Phone#_____Cost_____Available?____

Singing Telegram
Name_____Phone#_____Cost_____Available?____
Name_____Phone#_____Cost_____Available?____
Name_____Phone#_____Cost_____Available?____
Name_____Phone#_____Cost_____Available?____

Magician
Name_____Phone#_____Cost_____Available?____
Name_____Phone#_____Cost_____Available?____
Name_____Phone#_____Cost_____Available?____
Name_____Phone#_____Cost_____Available?____

Fortune Teller
Name_____Phone#_____Cost_____Available?____
Name_____Phone#_____Cost_____Available?____
Name_____Phone#_____Cost_____Available?____
Name_____Phone#_____Cost_____Available?____

Drummers
Name_____Phone#_____Cost_____Available?____
Name_____Phone#_____Cost_____Available?____
Name_____Phone#_____Cost_____Available?____
Name_____Phone#_____Cost_____Available?____

Your Unique Idea Here:_____

Name_____Phone#_____Cost_____Available?____
Name_____Phone#_____Cost_____Available?____
Name_____Phone#_____Cost_____Available?____
Name_____Phone#_____Cost_____Available?____

Another Brilliant Idea Here:_____

Name_____Phone#_____Cost_____Available?____
Name_____Phone#_____Cost_____Available?____
Name_____Phone#_____Cost_____Available?____
Name_____Phone#_____Cost_____Available?____

Your Clever Idea Here:_____

Name_____Phone#_____Cost_____Available?____
Name_____Phone#_____Cost_____Available?____
Name_____Phone#_____Cost_____Available?____
Name_____Phone#_____Cost_____Available?____

Another Unusual Idea Here:_____

Name_____Phone#_____Cost_____Available?____
Name_____Phone#_____Cost_____Available?____
Name_____Phone#_____Cost_____Available?____
Name_____Phone#_____Cost_____Available?____

X. When You've Decided, Put It Here

__ Ceremony Site Name:_____
  Address:_____
  Phone:_____ e-mail:_____
  Cost:_____

__Minister (Officiant):_____
  Phone:_____ e-mail:_____
  Cost:_____

__Reception Hall Name:_____
  Address:_____
  Phone:_____ e-mail:_____
  Cost:_____

__Wedding Coordinator Name:_____
  Phone:_____ e-mail:_____
  Cost:_____

__Disc Jockey Service:_____
  Name:_____
  Phone:_____ e-mail:_____
  Cost:_____

__Photographer Name:_____
  Phone:_____ e-mail:_____
  Cost:_____

__Videographer Name:_____
  Phone:_____ e-mail:_____
  Cost:_____

__Caterer Name:_____
  Phone:_____ e-mail:_____
  Cost:_____

__Limousine Service:_____
  Phone:_____ e-mail:_____
  Cost:_____

__Bakery Name:_____
  Address:_____
  Phone:_____ e-mail:_____
  Cost:_____

__Ice-Carver Name:_____
  Phone:_____ e-mail:_____
  Cost:_____

__Dove/Butterfly Release Operator:_____
  Phone:_____ e-mail:_____
  Cost:_____

__Vocalist:_____
  Phone:_____ e-mail:_____
  Cost:_____

__Dancers:_____
  Phone:_____ e-mail:_____
  Cost:_____

__Entertainment:_____
  Phone:_____ e-mail:_____
  Cost:_____

__Bagpiper:_____
  Phone:_____ e-mail:_____
  Cost:_____

__Musicians:_____
  Phone:_____ e-mail:_____
  Cost:_____

__Singing Telegram:_____
  Phone:_____ e-mail:_____
  Cost:_____

__Magician:_____
  Phone:_____ e-mail:_____
  Cost:_____

__Drummers:_____
  Phone:_____ e-mail:_____
  Cost:_____

Picture This!

Your wedding day will fly by so fast that it will seem like a dream. This is why pictures are so important. Once the moment is passed, you can't do it over again. For those of you who have hired a professional photographer, you are likely to get a lot of beautiful, professional photographs.

However, since photographers often charge by the picture and can't be everywhere at once, disposable cameras can be a fun supplement. It's also a great way to get some real gems of moments your professional may miss. On the down side, you are likely to get many under-exposed, useless pictures.

If you can't afford a professional, but do have a friend or two who have volunteered, here are some suggestions for posing, followed by a list of common photos. Add any photos that are not listed and cross off any that don't interest you. Use the list on the day-of to check off the ones you've done.

When posing group shots, avoid having people line up like tin soldiers. Arrange some people standing, some kneeling, some in front, and some in back. The bride has the luxury of always being in the center of each photograph. For formal gowns, be aware of having the train of her dress spread out in front of her. Also be aware of fingertips if people have their arms around each other or on each other's shoulders. It looks better to not see fingers at all, so just pull your hands back a little. If there are several bridesmaids, it looks very elegant to have their flowers placed around the edge of the bride's train, so the flowers face outward.

When taking a picture of the Groom, with the Bride's attendants, have the attendants sit at his feet. The same would be true for the picture of the Bride with the Groomsmen.

A suggestion for everyone: When having your picture taken, be aware of your chin. Most people have a tendency to either pull their chins in when they smile (giving them a double chin) or lifting their chins up (giving the camera a lovely view of their throats). A remedy? While keeping your chin level, move your chin forward slightly. If you overdo it, you'll get a chicken neck look. Not terribly attractive. If done without straining, you will be amazed at how the pictures will accurately reflect your natural radiant beauty.

Wedding Photo List

The Bride Always Gets To Be In The Center!

These are some suggestions. I hope they are helpful. If you have a professional photographer, you will probably be given a list to choose from. If not, here are some ideas. There's room at the bottom to add your own. Have fun!

____ Bride and Groom
____ Bride alone
____ Bride in Bride's room
____ Bride and Bridesmaids
____ Bride with Groomsmen
____ Bride with her parents
____ Bride with her mom
____ Bride with her dad
____ Groom Alone
____ Groom and Groomsmen
____ Groom and Bridesmaids
____ Groom with his parents
____ Groom with his mom
____ Groom with his dad
____ B & G with her parents
____ B & G with his parents
____ B & G with minister (officiant)
____ B & G with grandparents

____ _____

____ _____

____ _____

____ _____

____ B & G with flower/ring
____ Whole wedding party
____ B & G w/all her family
____ B & G w/all his family
____ Bride and Groom kissing
____ Bride's & Groom's rings
____ Close up of candle-lighting
____ Close up of wine ceremony
____ Signing Wedding License
____ G removing B's garter

Pictures Just For Fun
____ B's dad pointing fake shotgun at G
____ B's mom in witch's hat with G
____ G's mom in witch's hat with B
____ Groom with Ball & Chain

38

"The Belle Of The Ball "

Next we'll go to the part that interests brides the most: THE DRESS.

It can be quite disheartening for those on a *smaller* budget to go dress shopping. This author personally has trouble paying more for a dress (which I will only get to wear once for a few hours) than for a house payment. On the other hand, you don't want to start off the most important day of your life wearing your old bathrobe either.

A consignment shop is one place to start. These are places where people bring their one-time-worn dresses to be sold at significantly reduced prices. Outlets are also a great place to look. Another possibility (believe it or not) is thrift stores. Some people may choke on the idea, but there are a lot of beautiful dresses that end up there and sell for $100 or less. Bridesmaid dresses often show up here as well.

Another place to look for a dress is through the newspaper. It takes more time and patience, but those who sell them through the paper get fewer people looking at them and may be willing to sell them for less. I found a brand new, beautiful Jessica McClintocktm dress through the newspaper for $50. The previous owner ran a bridal shop and had used it as a display.

Veils also must be considered. Long or short, face covered or not, placed over your forehead or set back on your crown. It's a personal choice. Be creative. I had a five-tiered veil of lavender and white mesh (Stunning!) with a veil that covered my face. It was unusual, but brides get to make up their own rules. The only problem I had was that my sister spent an hour beforehand making my hair look beautiful, but you couldn't really see it under the veil. Ah, well, I knew it was there and I guess that's what counted.

You can choose from a wide assortment of pre-made veils or you can create one for yourself. Almost anyone who knows how to use a sewing machine can probably make a beautiful veil for you. I can't sew at all, but with a few supplies bought at a fabric and craft store, I saw how easily it came together. Find a friend who sews (if you don't) who will consider putting it together for you as a wedding gift.

For those who don't want to burden themselves with owning one, dresses and veils of all kinds can be rented for very reasonable prices. Whatever you choose, have fun!

XI. Decisions To Make:

Choosing Apparel/Accessories

Bridal Gown Preferences:
_____Time allotted to find perfect dress?
_____Color: White/Off-White or Other?
_____Length preferred? (Consider weather)
_____Veil?
<_____Over face or sitting in back?
<_____Color? (they don't have to be white)
<_____Length?
<_____Hand-made or bought? (easy to make)
<_____Style chosen for headpiece?
_____Slip needed?
_____Strapless bra needed?
_____Special nylons? (although no one can see them usually)
_____Girdle needed?
_____Garment bag for dress?
_____Person assigned to care for dress? (to take to cleaners after if need be)

Places to look:
_____Consignment shops checked?
_____Rental shops considered?
_____Newspaper ads (a great deal if you have the time to look)
_____Mail-order catalogs?

Other fashion considerations:
_____Having nails done?
_____Having hair done beforehand?
_____Two garters selected? (one to wear/one to throw)
_____Outfit for leaving on honeymoon?
_____Lingerie for honeymoon?
_____Wardrobe for honeymoon?

The Wedding Party:

_____Number of bridesmaids?
_____Matching dresses for them?
_____Will you be providing them?
_____Matching shoes for everyone? (think comfort too)
_____Flower girls?
_____Matching dresses for flower girls?
_____Dress styles chosen?
_____Are they providing their own dresses?
_____Men wearing tuxedos?
_____Are you having a ring bearer?
_____Will ring bearer really carry rings or just for show?
_____How many ushers will you need?
_____Who will they be? _____
_____Will you want them in tuxedos?
_____Will you want to give them boutonnieres?

Misc. Considerations:
_____Having rings engraved?
_____Flowers: real, silk or mixed?
_____Bouquets/Corsages/Boutonnieres: Make or buy?

XII. Things To Acquire

Clothing/Accessories:

Bride

Clothes:

_____ Dress
_____ Veil
_____ Underskirt
_____ Stockings
_____ Extra pair of stockings
_____ Shoes
_____ Two garters (one to keep/one to throw)
_____ Strapless bra
_____ Girdle
_____ New panties
_____ Garment bag for dress
_____ Lingerie for honeymoon
_____ Departing clothes
_____ Honeymoon clothes _____

_____ _____

_____ _____

Final Beauty Considerations:

_____ New lipstick
_____ Matching nail polish
_____ Bobby pins
_____ Safety pins (just in case)
_____ Hair spray
_____ Bouquet (for carrying)
_____ Bouquet (for throwing)
_____ Cloth handkerchief (trust me; you'll need it)
_____ Hand lotion

_____ _____

_____ _____

Groom

_____ Tuxedo
_____ Shirt
_____ Tie (clip or tie)
_____ Vest
_____ Cummerbund
_____ Cufflinks
_____ Tie Pin
_____ Shined shoes
_____ Black socks
_____ Silk Boxers/fancy underwear
_____ Boutonniere
_____ Cloth handkerchief (an absolute must!)
_____ Comb
_____ Departing (traveling) clothes
_____ Honeymoon clothes

_____ _____

_____ _____

Bridal party:

_____ Tuxedos for groomsmen
_____ Tuxedo for father(s)
_____ Boutonnieres for groomsmen/party
_____ Dresses for bridesmaids
_____ Shoes for bridesmaids
_____ Bouquet(s) (for bridesmaids)
_____ Dress(es) for flower girl(s)
_____ Suit/tux for ring bearer

"Let It Be Known . . ."

Creating a guest list and sending invitations can be stressful at best. Who should you invite? How many can the place hold? Will they come? Can we feed them all? Ugh. If you are having your affair catered, the task becomes even more difficult.

I suggest just brainstorming it. Put everyone in the world on the list, then try to whittle it down. It's fairly safe to assume that about half of the people you invite will show up. If you're having it catered, determine ahead of time how much you can afford to spend on food and divide it by the cost per person. Invite twice as many and cross your fingers. **A word to the wise: always order at least 25-30 more invitations than you plan on using.**

If you are having a buffet designed by a friend or parent with various people bringing food (as their wedding gift), then don't bother whittling the list down and invite everyone you'd like to see.

When you have the list of names the way you want them, start working on the addresses. Divide and conquer! Have your parents work on the distant relatives, your fiancé work on his side of the family, and your friends each collect a few. There's nothing scarier than thinking you have to do it all yourself!

Divide and conquer!

Unless you're only inviting two or three guests, you'll probably want to send them invitations. One inexpensive thing to do is to order them through the mail. You'll notice advertisements in bridal magazines, which offer high-quality invitations by mail at a fraction of the cost. Why spend hundreds of dollars on invitations when most people just throw them away anyway?

You can also make them up on a computer. The advantage is that it's inexpensive, but the downside is that you have to address all of the return envelopes yourself. You can order address labels or have a stamp made. Make sure the return envelopes have a postage stamp already on them. (The post office offers romantic stamps.)

One other thing; I would suggest sending the invitations about three weeks to a month in advance. Most people don't plan very far in advance and may possibly forget. It's hard to believe that your wedding is not on the forefront of everyone's minds (it should be!), but it's just not. Three weeks to a month is plenty of time, as long as your caterer has time to prepare.

XIII. Decisions to Make:

Invitations/Maps/Programs

_____Guest list written?

_____Addresses collected?

_____Computer-generated invitations?

_____Ordered by mail?

_____Invitation specialist? (stationary shop, etc.)

_____Number needed (25-30 more than you think--see previous page)

_____Return envelopes pre-printed?

_____Map drawn?

_____Copies made?

_____Copies cut?

_____Do you want programs?

_____Wedding Registry cards included?

_____Envelopes addressed?

_____Stamped?

_____Mailed? (**no earlier** than a month to six weeks before the wedding)

_____Is your return address pre-printed on envelopes?

_____Do you have return address labels?

_____Have you sent in announcement to newspaper?
(Call local newspaper and ask for the form to fill out.)

_____Are you expecting out-of-town guests?

_____Will they be housed with relatives?

_____Are there hotels nearby?

_____Are you paying for their stay?

_____Are reservations made?

A. Invitation Wording

Your Invitations can be worded a variety of ways, depending on your preference and your situation. Below are some examples. Note the addition of the phrases: 'Reception immediately following'. 'Mother of the Bride' and a phone number.

This is included so the guests can call the Mother of the Bride (in capitals because of the importance of this role) and ask about where the bride might be Registered, to ask any questions or to offer assistance.

If the Mother of the Bride is not part of the wedding plans, list someone who is and their phone number. You will probably not want to add your own number since it may seem tacky to personally ask the bride where she is Registered. Besides, it's one less thing for you to have to worry about.

Traditional

Mr. and Mrs. Peter Rabbit
Request the honour of your presence
At the marriage of their daughter
Ms. Bunny Rabbit
To
Mr. Jack Foot
Saturday, the tenth of August
Two thousand and one
At two o'clock
Briar Patch Church
Sacramento, California

RSVP by the seventeenth of July
Two thousand and six

Reception immediately following
Mother of the Bride
(916) 555-3476

Groom's Parents

Mr. and Mrs. Big Foot
Request the honour of your presence
At the marriage of
Ms. Bunny Rabbit
To their son
Jack Foot
(Etc.)

Contemporary Invitations

With contemporary invitations, there is a lot more room for creativity. If you would like more suggestions, visit a stationary store that sells invitations. There are many examples there. Here are a few to help you get the idea.

Bride and Groom's Parents

Mrs. and Mrs. Peter Rabbit
and
Mr. and Mrs. Big Foot
request the honour of your presence
at the marriage of their children
Bunny Rabbit
To
Jack Foot
(Etc.)

Bride and Groom

The honour of your presence
is requested at the marriage of
Bunny Rabbit
To
Jack Foot
(Etc.)

Bride's Parents

Mr. and Mrs. Peter Rabbit
would like you to
join with their daughter
Bunny
and
Jack Foot
as they celebrate their marriage on
(Etc.)

Both Parents

We invite you to share with us the
marriage of our children
Bunny Elaine
And
Jack Oliver
(Etc.)
Mr. and Mrs. Peter and Sally Rabbit
Mr. and Mrs. Big and Eva Foot
(Etc.)

Another Example

Bunny Rabbit
And
Jack Foot
Invite you to share in the celebration of the
beginning of their new life together when
they exchange their marriage vows on
Saturday, the tenth of August
At two o'clock
(Etc.)

B. Invitation Assignments

Invitations/Maps/Programs

Assigned to: Check when done:

_____	_____ Guest list written?
_____	_____ Addresses collected (Bride's)?
_____	_____ Addresses collected (Groom's)
_____	_____ Computer-generated invitations?
_____	_____ Ordered by mail?
_____	_____ Ordered from shop? (when?)
_____	_____ Number Ordered?
_____	_____ Return envelopes pre-printed?
_____	_____ Stamps purchased?
_____	_____ Map drawn?
_____	_____ Copies of map made?
_____	_____ Copies of map cut?
_____	_____ Gift Registry Cards Being Used?
_____	_____ Inserted in appropriate envelopes?
_____	_____ Hotel #'s/costs list made?
_____	_____ Copies of hotels made?
_____	_____ Inserted in appropriate envelopes?
_____	_____ Programs written?
_____	_____ Copies made?
_____	_____ Envelopes addressed?
_____	_____ Stamped?
_____	_____ Mailed?

The following pages can be used for making out your guest list. Tear the page out, make however many copies you need and assign each page a letter of the alphabet. List your guests alphabetically and it will be easier to keep track of RSVPs, how many are coming, what their gifts were, and if you sent a thank you note.

Invitation Mailed?____ Date _____ RSVP#_____

Name _____

Address_____

City/State/Zip _____

Thank You?_____ Date mailed_____ Gift _____

_____

_____

Invitation Mailed?____ Date _____ RSVP#_____

Name _____

Address_____

City/State/Zip _____

Thank You?_____ Date mailed_____ Gift _____

_____

_____

Invitation Mailed?____ Date _____ RSVP#_____

Name _____

Address_____

City/State/Zip _____

Thank You?_____ Date mailed_____ Gift _____

_____

_____

Invitation Mailed?____ Date _____ RSVP#_____

Name _____

Address_____

City/State/Zip _____

Thank You?_____ Date mailed_____ Gift _____

_____

_____

Invitation Mailed?____ Date _____ RSVP#_____

Name _____

Address_____

City/State/Zip _____

Thank You?_____ Date mailed_____ Gift _____

_____

_____

Invitation Mailed?____ Date _____ RSVP#_____

Name _____

Address_____

City/State/Zip _____

Thank You?_____ Date mailed_____ Gift _____

_____

_____

Invitation Mailed?___ Date _____ RSVP#_____

Name _____

Address_____

City/State/Zip _____

Thank You?____ Date mailed____ Gift _____

_____

_____

Invitation Mailed?___ Date _____ RSVP#_____

Name _____

Address_____

City/State/Zip _____

Thank You?____ Date mailed____ Gift _____

_____

_____

Invitation Mailed?___ Date _____ RSVP#_____

Name _____

Address_____

City/State/Zip _____

Thank You?____ Date mailed____ Gift _____

_____

_____

Invitation Mailed?___ Date _____ RSVP#_____

Name _____

Address_____

City/State/Zip _____

Thank You?____ Date mailed____ Gift _____

_____

_____

Invitation Mailed?___ Date _____ RSVP#_____

Name _____

Address_____

City/State/Zip _____

Thank You?____ Date mailed____ Gift _____

_____

_____

Invitation Mailed?___ Date _____ RSVP#_____

Name _____

Address_____

City/State/Zip _____

Thank You?____ Date mailed____ Gift _____

_____

_____

Invitation Mailed?____ Date _____ RSVP#_____

Name _____

Address_____

City/State/Zip _____

Thank You?_____ Date mailed_____ Gift _____

_____

_____

Invitation Mailed?____ Date _____ RSVP#_____

Name _____

Address_____

City/State/Zip _____

Thank You?_____ Date mailed_____ Gift _____

_____

_____

Invitation Mailed?____ Date _____ RSVP#_____

Name _____

Address_____

City/State/Zip _____

Thank You?_____ Date mailed_____ Gift _____

_____

_____

Invitation Mailed?____ Date _____ RSVP#_____

Name _____

Address_____

City/State/Zip _____

Thank You?_____ Date mailed_____ Gift _____

_____

_____

Invitation Mailed?____ Date _____ RSVP#_____

Name _____

Address_____

City/State/Zip _____

Thank You?_____ Date mailed_____ Gift _____

_____

_____

Invitation Mailed?____ Date _____ RSVP#_____

Name _____

Address_____

City/State/Zip _____

Thank You?_____ Date mailed_____ Gift _____

_____

_____

Invitation Mailed?____ Date _____ RSVP#_____

Name _____

Address_____

City/State/Zip _____

Thank You?_____ Date mailed_____ Gift _____

_____

_____

Invitation Mailed?____ Date _____ RSVP#_____

Name _____

Address_____

City/State/Zip _____

Thank You?_____ Date mailed_____ Gift _____

_____

_____

Invitation Mailed?____ Date _____ RSVP#_____

Name _____

Address_____

City/State/Zip _____

Thank You?_____ Date mailed_____ Gift _____

_____

_____

Invitation Mailed?____ Date _____ RSVP#_____

Name _____

Address_____

City/State/Zip _____

Thank You?_____ Date mailed_____ Gift _____

_____

_____

Invitation Mailed?____ Date _____ RSVP#_____

Name _____

Address_____

City/State/Zip _____

Thank You?_____ Date mailed_____ Gift _____

_____

_____

Invitation Mailed?____ Date _____ RSVP#_____

Name _____

Address_____

City/State/Zip _____

Thank You?_____ Date mailed_____ Gift _____

_____

_____

XIV. Things To Acquire:

Invitations/Maps/Programs

_____Invitations
_____Envelopes (if invitations are hand-made)
_____Stamps
_____Return Address labels (they're worth the extra few bucks)
_____Gift Registry Cards
_____Thank-You Notes
_____Maps
_____Programs
_____Guest list
_____Reservations for out-of-town guests
_____Names & phone numbers of local hotels (for guests)
_____Names & phone numbers of relatives who will temporarily adopt guests

Decorating Doozies

For those Martha Stewarts out there, decorating for your wedding reception is just a matter of a clip here, a snip there and a little food coloring. I envy you. For the rest of us whose talents lie elsewhere, it's still possible to create a sensational ambiance without a whole lot of artistic know-how.

A theme reception is a nice way to go. A Mardi Gras theme is one example. You can get some feathered masks, ticker-tape type streamers, and lots of little plastic toys. Maybe you'd like a Hawaiian theme with hula dancers, grass skirts, and a luau. The idea of a garden wedding can include carnations on the tables, bright colored napkins and flowers everywhere. For a theme wedding, you can go as far as your imagination will take you. See the section on theme weddings on page #17.

There are other ways to create a personal touch at your reception. Put pictures of you and your beloved set by the guest book. Perhaps make a whole table consisting of pictures of the happy couple, the matte on a picture for your guests to sign wishing you well, and maybe a honeymoon (money) tree. A basket for cards is nice too.

> ## A theme reception is a nice way to go.

Here's another suggestion: Most people have a story to tell about how they became engaged. Write it up. Embellish it. Make it funny. You can write one version that's the bride's and one that's from the groom's point of view. To the bride, perhaps you were thinking it was just a nice night out to dinner. He was being very attentive while you talked. Then, out of the blue, a woman comes in dressed like a fairy godmother, sings you a song and says your honey has something to say. His version might be more like this: I took her out to dinner. She was talking about something, but I wasn't really listening. When would that singing telegram GET here! Etc. You get the idea. Your guests will find it amusing and it makes a nice keepsake.

There's one other thing I wanted to mention about when you're setting things up - if you are having a buffet dinner, make sure that people can move down *both* sides of the table. Waiting in line for food is no fun. I suggest placing several tables around the room, each with its own variety of food. A vegetarian table is a nice touch.

Your wedding can be fun with feathers or bouncy with balloons. You can coordinate your colors or create a rainbow of radiance. Whatever you decide, allow it to be a reflection of you. You're doing a great job, so relax and enjoy this latest phase of your creation.

XV. Decisions To Make:

Decorations, Utensils, Etc.

Food-related Needs:
_____Napkins with your names & date?
_____Punch bowls provided?
_____Toasting glasses: bought, rented, or provided?
_____Engraved? (for Bride and Groom)
_____Plates/cups/silverware: rented, provided or paper?

General Needs:
_____Gift table?
_____Pictures of Bride/Groom on gift table?
_____Guest book?
_____Guest book attendant? (friend or employed)
_____Pen with plume? (feather)
_____Money tree?

Table Needs:
_____How many tables needed?
_____Tables provided?
_____Renting?
_____Tablecloths provided?
_____How many will you need?
_____Cloth or throwaway?
_____Candles? (on tables)
_____Disposable Cameras? (on tables)
_____Favors for the guests?
_____Centerpieces provided? (see suggestions)

Decoration Needs:
_____Balloons?
_____Flower arrangements?
_____Computerized banner?
_____Aisle runner?
_____Archway: bought, rented or balloons?
_____Ice-Carving?

Unusual Wedding/Reception Entertainment

Miss Manners may not agree with me, but I think that having some sort of entertainment during the wedding is a great idea. Let's start with the more common forms of entertainment: A vocalist. Having a professional vocalist singing 'your song' during the ceremony makes a special impression. Many people invite their cousin Matilda (or whoever) to sing a song on their special day. Sometimes this works out fine, but often the person chosen has never sung in public before or has and should stop immediately. You've gone to great lengths to make this a perfect day, why settle for anything less than a great singer?

You can also have a harpist, flutist or banjo player. The first two create an elegant, spiritual feeling; the last one would be just plain fun. Local colleges can offer a nice selection of string quartets, or other serious musicians.

Another idea for entertainment addresses the concept of a theme wedding. How about a bagpiper and a troupe of Highland Dancers? You can find schools for almost any style of dance: Hawaiian, tap, country line, jazz, square-dancing, whatever. The students there would love an opportunity to perform and will do so usually for a very modest fee. (I paid $50 for some terrific Highland Dancers.) They only need to perform for a little over half an hour while you're out having bridal party pictures taken.

Be a little crazy.

You may want to consider having a singing entertainer who will interact with the audience, tell jokes and sing like crazy. Or hire a magician who can razzle-dazzle them. Maybe as part of the ambiance, you can hire a psychic who will tell people's fortunes. If you're having a renaissance wedding, have a jester entertain the court.

Another thing, which can be really fun, is to hire a singing telegram performer to come and sing to your new spouse. It could be something romantic (like an elegantly dressed person coming in to sing a special song). Maybe something funny (like having the groom arrested or someone coming in saying she was stood up for a date). Or perhaps something silly (like someone dressed in a big dinosaur costume) could be really funny.

Have fun with it. Be a little crazy. It's your day; you're the star, so let your light so shine!

The Very Definition Of Reception Activities

(In Order Of Occurrence)

The Grand Re-Entrance: After the magnificent event, the couple goes somewhere t take bridal pictures. If you have a Disc Jockey or announcer, that person will announce the bridesmaids and groomsmen by name (sometimes the ring bearers/flower girls, but this isn't necessary). The bridesmaids and groomsmen usually enter in pairs to some party music. When they're all in and after a dramatic pause, the DJ announces the bride and groom's entrance into society as a newly married couple. Much fanfare.

Couple Says A Few Words: It is customary for the bride and groom to take a few minutes to issue a warm welcome to all the guests and thank them for coming. Maybe come up with something about how their presence means so much to you, blah blah blah. You get the idea. Whatever your heart prompts you to say. Or they can wait until the end of all the toasts. The bride and groom are frequently the last ones to make a toast. It just depends on how your wedding happens to be flowing.

Receiving Line: A receiving line is time-consuming and not terribly interesting. It's far more personal for the bride and groom to float around the room (on cloud nine, of course) and issue warm hellos and friendly small talk as they go. If you do decide to have one say, to include family members who otherwise might be ignored, be sure everyone knows where they are to stand and allow room for people to enter the reception without *having* to stand in the receiving line if they don't want to.

Eat: I don't think this part needs a lot of explaining. The bride and groom eat first, followed by the bridal party, close family members, then the guests. It is not unusual for the catering staff or a close friend to prepare the food for the bride and groom. Sometimes a DJ may release the tables one at a time or the catering staff might do it. Some DJs make people stand up and sing a song to the couple for their supper.

Best Man's Toast: The best man usually does the first toast. This happens usually people have finished eating, but before any of the other events. Be sure he knows this well ahead of time. This is the chance for him to talk kindly about the groom, perhaps mention how he heard about the couple meeting, tell a cute story, and especially be really clear that marrying the bride is the best thing that ever happened to the groom.

All Other Toasts: Frequently, the Maid of Honor, Father of the Bride and Father of the Groom make toasts. Actually, anyone who has something nice to say to the couple should be encouraged to speak. When else in your life are you going to get the chance to be in a large group of people who all have something nice to say about you?

Bouquet Toss: This is usually done after people have finished eating. The bouquet toss is done first. The bride uses a bouquet that was created just for throwing (not the one she carried down the aisle), stands with her back to the unmarried women and tosses it over her shoulder to them. It is not unusual to lean one's throw to someone in the group who is already engaged or nearing that point. It is also a good idea to limit the participants to those of marriageable age.

Garter Toss: For this purpose, the bride is wearing an extra garter. Some people put one on each leg and some put both on one leg, with the throwing garter being the easiest to get. A big production is made out of the groom getting the garter off of the bride's leg. Some grooms dive under their beloved's dress and emerge with the garter in their teeth. Once retrieved, the groom turns his back on the single men gathered before him and flings it over his shoulder. Don't be surprised if the men don't jump at it. Often, they will hurriedly push the engaged men to the front. Cowards.

Cake-Cutting - This is done shortly after the garter toss. The couple-du-jour slice the cake to the tune of something appropriate (like the theme from 'Jaws'). It's polite to feed each other a piece of cake. Some people do the whole smooshing the cake in each other's face thing, but I'm not too in favor of that. If my beloved had smooshed cake in my perfectly done-up face and gotten frosting all over the most beautiful dress I've ever owned on my most special day of days, there would be hell to pay. If you feel the same way, I'd be sure to let your groom in on it.

First Dance: The first dance is something that some brides and many grooms dread. When the music starts playing, the bride and groom are the only ones on the floor. My beloved groom and I took lessons beforehand to learn how to waltz together. We had a song picked out ('Could I have this dance?' by Anne Murray) and the dance steps rehearsed. It wasn't perfect, but who would dare criticize the bride and groom on their best day? Sometimes, parents and family are invited up during the middle of the song. It really depends how comfortable the newlyweds are being in the limelight.

Father/Daughter -- Mother/Son Dance: These are often the next two dances in line. The bride dances with her father (or father figure) and the groom with his mother. Sometimes, the father/daughter (or mother/son) couple starts on the dance floor alone, then invites others to join them on the floor. The song, 'Butterfly Kisses' is a great song for this dance.

Money Dance: This is a dance where the bride and groom dance with a variety of partners who pay for the privilege of dancing with them. I call it the 'Honeymoneymoon' dance. The money received is either stuffed into or pinned onto the newlywed's clothing or the bride carries a small purse. (I suggest the purse.) The dance usually lasts for several songs, depending how many people are waiting to dance. I personally prefer to have a Honeymoon (money) Tree put discreetly on a table off to the side. Open dancing follows this dance.

The Departure: It's customary for the bride and groom to leave the reception when there are still enough people to wish them on their way. Most people change clothes before they go (tuxes are usually rented & dresses need to be cleaned or aren't comfy for riding around in). When you decide to leave, people should have access to either birdseed or bubbles to send you on your way. People often end up using the bubbles during the first dance, but have a towel to wipe it up so nobody slips. Rose petals from your local florist or funeral director might make for a fragrant goodbye. Birdseed is nice and the birds appreciate the free meal. Be sure someone is assigned to distribute this.

XVI. Decisions To Make:

Reception Activities

Bride/Groom:

_____Do you want a head table?

_____Bride/Groom move around greeting guests?

_____Receiving line?

_____Bride/Groom say a few words to welcome guests?

Reception Events:

_____Entertainment while you're taking pictures? (see page 54)

_____Toast by Best Man?

_____Toast by Maid of Honor?

_____Toast by Father of Bride?

_____Toast by Father of Groom?

_____Any other toasts?

_____First dance? (Bride/Groom)

_____Father/Daughter --- Mother/Son dance?

_____Money dance?

_____Special songs wanted for these?

_____Karaoke? (of questionable success)

Departure Considerations:

_____Couple leaving right after or during reception?

_____Would you like to bring wedding food with you?

_____Someone assigned to prepare departing food for you?

_____Do you have something to put it in? (Sealed plastic/picnic basket)

_____Couple changing first or staying in wedding garb?

_____Bird seed for couple's departure?

_____Bubbles for couple's departure?

_____Rose petals for couple's departure?

_____Several people assigned for clean up?

_____Someone assigned to pay wedding service professionals?

_____Someone keeping track of signed wedding license?

_____Do you have any designated drivers, if needed, for your guests?

XVII. Decisions To Make: Food

_____Catered?

_____Brought by friends?

_____Schedule for time frame to serve food?

_____Is there flexibility?

_____Lunch/Dinner/Finger Foods? (make list)

_____Punch?

_____Sodas?

_____Alcohol wanted?

_____Food coordinator chosen? (<u>not you!</u>)

_____Table diagram with what food goes where?

_____Vegetarian-only table?

_____Helpers to put out the food?

_____Back-up extra food (chips, dip, etc.)

_____Matching trays?

_____Snacks on tables?

Cake:

_____Cake flavor?

_____Cake style?

_____Frosting? (whipped cream or otherwise)

_____Who is making it?

_____Special cake top?

_____Saving top layer of cake?

_____Someone assigned to put top layer in fridge/freezer for you?

XVIII. Things To Acquire:
Reception Needs

Decorative:

_____ Balloons
_____ Helium tank (disposable/rented)
_____ Tablecloths
_____ Centerpieces
_____ Disposable cameras on tables
_____ Favors for guests
_____ Streamers
_____ Banners (Computer-generated is inexpensive)
_____ Flowers
_____ Pictures of Bride/Groom on gift table

_____ _____

_____ _____

_____ _____

Food-related:

_____ Cake topper
_____ Napkins (engraved with name)
_____ Napkins (regular)
_____ Plates
_____ Cups
_____ Toasting Glasses (guests)
_____ Toasting Glasses (Bride/Groom)
_____ Forks
_____ Knives
_____ Special knife to cut cake
_____ Spoons
_____ Serving spoons
_____ Punch Bowl
_____ Coffee pot
_____ Tea pot
_____ Condiments

_____ Microwave
_____ Coolers

_____ _____

_____ _____

_____ _____

_____ _____

Miscellaneous:
_____ Bird seed for departure
_____ Bubbles for departure
_____ Speaker set-up (if no Disc Jockey)
_____ Microphone (if no Disc Jockey)
_____ Cellular phone for emergencies
_____ Honeymoon (money) tree
_____ Large garbage bags (brightly colored is nice) for clean up
_____ Soap/streamers/signs/cans/etc. for getaway car
_____ Location/availability of nearest store for emergencies
_____ Put some of YOUR snazzy ideas here:

_____ _____

_____ _____

_____ _____

_____ _____

_____ _____

_____ _____

A. Food Staples

_____ Coffee
_____ Tea
_____ Sugar/sugar substitute
_____ Honey
_____ Cream
_____ Cake
_____ Condiments
_____ Ice-cream (for punch)
_____ Frozen punch/concentrated punch
_____ Sprite/7-up etc. (lots - for punch)
_____ Ice
_____ Toasting drink (champagne/sparkling grape)
_____ Snacks on tables
_____ Alcohol
_____ Sodas
_____ Your delightful suggestions here:

_____ _____

_____ _____

_____ _____

_____ _____

_____ _____

_____ _____

_____ _____

B. Food Suggestions

_____ Candy kisses on tables
_____ M & M's
_____ Sandwich makings
_____ Fruit compote
_____ Potato/macaroni salad
_____ Finger foods - hot and cold (make separate list)
_____ Pasta
_____ Cheese/meat tray
_____ Chips/dip
_____ Vegetable tray w/dip
_____ Olives
_____ Nuts
_____ Devilled eggs
_____ Ham
_____ Turkey
_____ Pre-cut roast beef wrapped around pickles/cream cheese
_____ Meatballs
_____ Cookies
_____ Vegetarian dishes
_____ Rolls
_____ Jell-O cups (kids love 'em)
_____ More room for your amazing ideas:

_____ _____

_____ _____

_____ _____

_____ _____

_____ _____

_____ _____

Some Helpful Hints For the Day of:

1. **Delegate!** **Delegate!** **Delegate!**   This is important and warrants repeating often. Allow others to pamper you on your special day. Your only job is looking beautiful walking down that aisle to your beloved. That's it! Allow everyone else to do the rest.

2. Flower Girl/Ring Bearer should be at least four or five years old to avoid problems. If they are younger, but you really want them to do it, have a parent or grandparent sitting in the first or second row to encourage them and give them arms to run in to.

3. If you are having a candle-lighting ceremony, have matches ready and be sure the candle has been lit beforehand to melt the wax off the wick.

4. If it might be windy, have a wind guard ready for the candle. Or you can just go through the ceremony and *pretend* there is a flame.

5. For the wine ceremony, have a table there to put the wineglass on and some kind of liquid for the ceremony. If you don't drink alcohol, water is an acceptable alternative. If you prefer wine, white wine is less likely to stain (if perchance there is a spill). Also, mark the champagne 'for toast only' so it doesn't get used for the punch by accident.

6. Bride and Groom should each carry a hanky to the altar for teary eyes or runny noses. (Bride can carry it with her flowers.) Wiping your nose on your sleeve is even less attractive than it sounds and makes for a terrible picture.

7. **Make someone else in charge of the wedding license and of payments.** You have enough to worry about on your special day. This is usually the best man's job, but you may ask someone else you can also trust.

8. A Disc Jockey really helps keep a reception moving. If not, have a P.A. system of some sort and ask someone to be in charge of making announcements. Some people wait for the cake cutting and other events before making their departure, so it would be rude to keep them waiting.

9. Have snacks available for your guests while you are taking your pictures.

10. Some sort of entertainment for your guests during this time is also a thoughtful gesture. Refer to the list of unusual entertainment. (page #56)

XIX. Wedding Helper Assignment Sheet

For the Reception:	Assigned To:	Done:
Caterer/food preparation	_____	_____
Making punch	_____	_____
Making coffee	_____	_____
Decorating	_____	_____
Decorating	_____	_____
Decorating	_____	_____
Decorating	_____	_____
Arranging flowers	_____	_____
Buying alcohol	_____	_____
Putting out tablecloths	_____	_____
Putting out tablecloths	_____	_____
Putting out tablecloths	_____	_____
Guest book attendant	_____	_____
Creating centerpieces	_____	_____
Making traveling food for B&G	_____	_____
Returning Tuxedos Afterwards	_____	_____
Have Bridal gown cleaned	_____	_____
Clean-up	_____	_____
Clean-up	_____	_____
Clean-up	_____	_____
Clean-up	_____	_____
Any Last Minute Things	_____	_____
_____	_____	_____
_____	_____	_____
_____	_____	_____
_____	_____	_____
_____	_____	_____

XX. Wedding Helper Check-Off List:

Reception Day-Of Details

Set-up:

_____ Ask (assign tasks to) people (guests/friends/relatives) to help you.

_____ Ask for help moving chairs if necessary.

_____ Tablecloths on tables?

_____ Centerpieces on tables?

_____ Cameras on tables?

_____ Decorations put up?

_____ Bathrooms look nice?

_____ Guest book and pen out?

_____ Someone assigned to guest book sign-in detail?

_____ Chairs set up?

_____ Space for dance floor?

_____ Table, ashtrays, chairs outside for smokers

_____ Minister ready to go?

Food:

_____ Snacks on tables?

_____ Punch made?

_____ Is food all there?

_____ Make sure cake is set up.

_____ Start coffee.

_____ Put on hot water for tea.

_____ Put out cream/sugar/honey.

_____ Put out plates, napkins & silverware.

_____ Put out special knife for cutting cake.

_____ Have a glass of warm water available for cake knife

_____ Toasting drink (champagne, etc.) is kept separate & well marked.

_____ Put out soda/beer, etc.

_____ Is there enough ice? (if not, send someone to nearest store)

Miscellaneous:

_____ Check music volume.

_____ Assign someone to decorate the getaway car

_____ Make sure wedding license is signed.

_____ Put someone in charge of caring for wedding gifts.

XXI. Decisions to Make: Miscellaneous

Before the wedding/honeymoon:

_____Prenuptial agreement needed? (two families)

_____Having an engagement photo?

_____Planning to attend any bridal shows?

_____Have you registered for gifts?

_____Will you need traveler's checks for honeymoon?

_____Need film/camera for honeymoon?

_____Buying your new spouse a present to give on honeymoon?

_____Will you want your flowers preserved?

_____Do you have a back-up person to coordinate/delegate?

_____Do you have a friend to be a designated driver for intoxicated guests?

The wedding/honeymoon itself:

_____Renting a car?

_____Hiring a limousine?

_____Do you want to bring wedding food for your trip?

_____Video camera wanted?

_____Tickets needed?

During your absence from home:

_____Have your mail stopped while you're gone?

_____Animals/plants to care for in your absence?

_____Newspaper stopped while you're gone?

_____Child care while gone? (Leave signed emergency medical slips for each child.)

After your return:

_____Need to call social security for new card?

_____Link bank accounts yet?

_____Gift-opening party after honeymoon?

_____Thank you cards bought?

_____List kept of who gave what?

XXII. Bride's Honeymoon Checklist

_____Lingerie packed
_____Bathing suits
_____Towels
_____Dressy clothes
_____Casual clothes
_____Camera
_____Film
_____Video camera
_____Sunglasses
_____Honeymoon gift for husband
_____Passport
_____Marriage license (if needed)
_____Oils, lotions, personal toys, etc.
_____Cash & credit cards
_____Birth Control

_____ _____

_____ _____

_____ _____

_____ _____

_____ _____

XXIII. Groom's Honeymoon Checklist

Essentials:

_____ Destination determined
_____ Maps
_____ Tickets
_____ Money
_____ Reservation confirmation
_____ Gas in car
_____ Air in tires
_____ Car washed
_____ Luggage packed
_____ List of all phone numbers
_____ Let at least one person have all the numbers in case of an emergency.
_____ Film for honeymoon
_____ Honeymoon gift for spouse
_____ Traveler's checks for honeymoon
_____ Auto Club card (in case of any breakdowns)
_____ Passport
_____ Film/camera
_____ Phone card

Romantic touches:

_____ Have roses waiting in room.
_____ Have can of whipped cream waiting in room. (naughty, naughty!)
_____ Cassette/CD of Bride's favorite music ready in car.
_____ Call destination so they know you are a honeymoon couple.
_____ Put some of your fantastic suggestions here:

_____ _____

_____ _____

_____ _____

Cutting Corners

When the issue of money comes up, tempers flair, emotions run wild and general pandemonium breaks out. This is usually because everything always costs more than the person with the money wants to spend. Whether this is because you don't have much money to spend or you just want to keep costs down, it's important to make a budget and stick to it. The next section is an outline to help you arrange your budget.

Some things you can't get around, like the cost of the wedding license. Flowers, however, are more flexible. Silk flowers cost far less than fresh flowers and flowers from a good friend's garden don't cost anything at all. You may even want to mix fresh and silk. There are places that will rent you silk flowers at far less than it would cost to buy them.

Another area people get carried away is with centerpieces. You can make beautiful centerpieces with helium balloons, single candles with something glued on for decoration or you can take cheap glass flower vases (like the kind flower delivery places use) at thrift stores, wrap colored tissue around it and tie it with a bow. If you put pinwheels in them, you have artfully combined a fun gift for any attendance. (The adults too.) your centerpiece with children in have fun with them

THE LESS YOU HAVE TO DO YOURSELF, THE LOWER YOUR STRESS WILL BE.

If you can't afford videographer, have a camera tape the event. you ought to have two. a professional friend with a video Or better yet, maybe The whole event will later seem like a blur if you don't get it on video. Besides, some people are more comfortable behind a camera lens than they are mingling and would love to do it.

Oh, and when you find a hall, try to find a place that includes tables and chairs. If this isn't possible, then you'll have to rent them.

Another huge expense is the bride's dress. Please shop around. Consignment stores offer amazing deals, as do newspaper ads and ebay. If you feel you must have it new, then look at the outlet stores for your gown.

The biggest expense is the food. Remember that your friends and family love you and want very much to help. Don't be afraid to ask. You may be surprised by how delighted they are to be included.

XXIV. Budget Records

Expense	$How Much Budgeted$	$How Much Spent$
Ceremony Needs:		
Hall	$_____	$_____
Aisle runner	$_____	$_____
Invitations	$_____	$_____
Flowers	$_____	$_____
Bouquets	$_____	$_____
Boutonnieres	$_____	$_____
Corsages	$_____	$_____
Rings	$_____	$_____
Engraving	$_____	$_____
Rehearsal dinner	$_____	$_____
Candles/Matches	$_____	$_____
Wine Goblet/Wine	$_____	$_____
Ribbons	$_____	$_____
Wedding license	$_____	$_____
Ring pillow	$_____	$_____
_____	$_____	$_____
Decorations:		
Balloons	$_____	$_____
Streamers	$_____	$_____
Flowers	$_____	$_____
Centerpieces	$_____	$_____
Party favors	$_____	$_____
Bird Seed/Bubbles	$_____	$_____
Cameras For Tables	$_____	$_____
Honeymoon ($) Tree	$_____	$_____
Tablecloths	$_____	$_____
Archway	$_____	$_____
Gazebo	$_____	$_____
_____	$_____	$_____

Wedding Professionals:

Minister	$_____	$_____
Videographer	$_____	$_____
Photographer	$_____	$_____
Reception Entertainment	$_____	$_____
Disc Jockey	$_____	$_____
Caterer	$_____	$_____
Musicians	$_____	$_____
Dove/Butterfly release	$_____	$_____
Ice-carving	$_____	$_____
Wedding Coordinator	$_____	$_____
Limousine Service	$_____	$_____
Bakery (cake)	$_____	$_____
Vocalist	$_____	$_____
Dancers	$_____	$_____
Bagpiper	$_____	$_____
Singing Telegram	$_____	$_____
Magician	$_____	$_____
Drummers	$_____	$_____
_____	$_____	$_____
_____	$_____	$_____

General Needs:

Stamps	$_____	$_____
Return Address Labels	$_____	$_____
Thank-you notes	$_____	$_____
Honeymoon film	$_____	$_____
Masking/duct tape	$_____	$_____
Guest book/pen	$_____	$_____
_____	$_____	$_____
_____	$_____	$_____
_____	$_____	$_____

Apparel:

Hers

Dress	$_____	$_____
Underskirt	$_____	$_____
Veil	$_____	$_____
Shoes	$_____	$_____
Undergarments	$_____	$_____
Make-up	$_____	$_____
Nails	$_____	$_____
Traveling Outfit	$_____	$_____
_____	$_____	$_____

His

Tuxedo/shoes	$_____	$_____
Tuxedo Shirt	$_____	$_____
Cuff Links	$_____	$_____
Traveling outfit	$_____	$_____
Handkerchief	$_____	$_____
Silk boxers	$_____	$_____
_____	$_____	$_____

Wedding Party

Flower Girl	$_____	$_____
Bridesmaids	$_____	$_____

Honeymoon

Tickets	$_____	$_____
Hotel	$_____	$_____
Bed & Breakfast	$_____	$_____
Spending Money	$_____	$_____
Rental Car	$_____	$_____
Film	$_____	$_____

Total Food Allotment $_____ $_____

Food
Caterer $_____ $_____
Cheese/meat trays $_____ $_____
Fruit trays $_____ $_____
Chips $_____ $_____
Rolls/bread $_____ $_____
Condiments $_____ $_____

Your delightful menu here:

_____ $_____ $_____
_____ $_____ $_____
_____ $_____ $_____
_____ $_____ $_____
_____ $_____ $_____
_____ $_____ $_____
_____ $_____ $_____
_____ $_____ $_____
_____ $_____ $_____
_____ $_____ $_____
_____ $_____ $_____
_____ $_____ $_____
_____ $_____ $_____
_____ $_____ $_____
_____ $_____ $_____
_____ $_____ $_____
_____ $_____ $_____
_____ $_____ $_____
_____ $_____ $_____
_____ $_____ $_____
_____ $_____ $_____
                          $_____ $_____

Food-Related:

Cake	$_____	$_____
Cake top	$_____	$_____
Guest toasting glasses	$_____	$_____
Bride/Groom glasses	$_____	$_____
Special knife for cake	$_____	$_____
Alcohol	$_____	$_____
Sparkling Cider	$_____	$_____
Punch bowls	$_____	$_____
Plates	$_____	$_____
Cold drink cups	$_____	$_____
Hot drink cups	$_____	$_____
Forks/knives/spoons	$_____	$_____
Coolers	$_____	$_____
Napkins engraved	$_____	$_____
Napkins regular	$_____	$_____
Sugar/cream, etc.	$_____	$_____
Coffee pot rental	$_____	$_____
Coffee	$_____	$_____
_____	$_____	$_____
_____	$_____	$_____
_____	$_____	$_____
_____	$_____	$_____
_____	$_____	$_____
_____	$_____	$_____
_____	$_____	$_____
_____	$_____	$_____
_____	$_____	$_____
	$_____	$_____

Appendix

The Words You've All Been Waiting For!...

This next section has one of the most personal parts of your wedding day; the ceremony. It starts off with a checklist to help you remember what order the ceremony is done. It's also very helpful to keep track of which parts you've chosen and where they go. If you have plans to add music in the middle, it's good for the D.J. to know what's happening. A wedding coordinator might also like this information, as well as the minister you choose.

Most of the parts have a special meaning, a reason for being there -- a purpose. Some parts are just really pretty words. It's up to you how you want the ceremony to go. There's no part that specifically _has_ to be there, so just go with what feels comfortable. Take what you like and leave the rest, as long as there is something that asks if they want to be married and they say yes. Most ceremonies are 15-20 minutes.

Use the 'Order of Ceremony Worksheet' page as a guide for putting together your special ceremony. It's listed in the order ceremonies usually go. Fill in the number of each part you like before tearing out the pages. It's less likely you'll lose any that way. Or you can tear out the pages and move them around if you like. Some people find they may like more than one Benediction, so they move one of them where a reading might go - to break up the Candle-lighting & Wine ceremony. I do find that it works best to pronounce marriage and present the new couple at the end. After you announce the couple as being married, people start applauding and stop listening. When you get it the way you want, you may want to make a copy, then put it aside for the officiant, along with the worksheet that has all the important phone numbers and directions to the wedding site.

The first part is called 'The Gathering Words'. It can also be called the 'introductory statement', the 'greeting' or whatever. Its purpose is to greet the guests, talk a little about why everybody decided to gather together, and what marriage is all about. You can choose one, several, or just parts. Feel free to re-arrange the sentences, the wording or anything else you'd like. The goal is to have the ceremony reflect who you two are as a couple and what your marriage means to you.

XXV. Order Of Ceremony Worksheet

Name(s)_____Same Last Name?_____

Date of Wedding_____ Time_____

Wedding Site Address_____

Directions:_____

_____

_____

Home Phone:_____Event Phone_____

Cell Phone:_____E-mail_____

Deposit Paid_____Balance Due_____

_____

_____

_____Gathering Words_____

_____Opening Prayer/Blessing_____

_____Support From Families   Bride_____Groom_____

_____Charge To Couple_____

_____Consent_____

_____Candle-lighting Ceremony_____

_____Readings or Song_____

_____Wine Ceremony_____

_____Vows_____

_____Guest Participation of Vows_____

_____Promises_____

_____Renewing of Promises_____

_____Family Promises_____

_____Affirmation of the Community_____

_____Rings_____

_____Concluding Blessing_____

_____Benediction_____

_____Ribbon Ceremony _____

_____Dove/Butterfly Release_____

_____Marriage Pronouncement_____

_____Breaking the Glass_____

_____Presentation of Couple_____

Gathering Words #1

Hello & welcome. We are here to witness the creation of a marriage. Marriage is the most intimate of all relationships. It is the ultimate commitment to love, share, trust and grow with another person. It is the beginning of a whole new life.

By entering into this marriage _____ & _____ are stating publicly, the feelings and commitments they have held privately between them. They are proclaiming their love for, their trust in and their loyalty to the one they cherish above all others.

Marriage has been described as living in love with your best friend. Love is one of the few constants in the universe. It is reality, affinity and communication. Only love is capable of joining living beings by their deepest essence, uniting, completing and fulfilling them.

Marriage is a symbol of the commitment to create a lifelong partnership based on love.

Gathering Words #2

We have been invited here today to witness and celebrate the uniting in marriage of _____ & _____.   They are taking the first step of their new beginning; their new life together.

The ability and desire for one human being to love another is perhaps the most precious and fulfilling gift that has been entrusted to us. It is an all-consuming task, a lifelong endeavor -- the journey we've been preparing for all of our lives.

Loving someone is a reason to stretch beyond our limits, to become for the sake of the other. It is to look into the soul of your beloved and accept what you see. Loving is the ultimate commitment which challenges humans to become all that we are meant to be.

As they join in marriage today, _____ & _____ are announcing to the world that they are welcoming that challenge.

Gathering Words #3

Hello and welcome! May your hearts be glad and your spirits be light. For every thing there is a season and a time for every purpose under Heaven. Now is the time for a wedding.

_____ & _____ have asked you all here today to bear witness to the forming of their covenant. In honor of this event, they will say heartfelt words, perform age-old rituals and validate this event in your presence, their family and friends. They will laugh and cry, dance and sing, and above all else, celebrate their love with the blessings of the people who matter most to them.

To this day _____ & _____ bring the joy in their hearts as a gift to one another. They bring their shared dreams, which tie them together. And they bring the seeds for their future, out of which will grow their life together.

You have been invited to share in their joy because of your bonds to the bride and groom and their families. Again, they welcome you and thank you for coming.

Gathering Words #4

Hello everyone and welcome. Thank you for joining us on this day of gladness and good fortune.

_____ & _____ have come together to publicly proclaim their undying love through the celebration of their marriage.

We are all here to learn about loving and being loved, and to watch the miracle of love exchanged enriches every one of us. Therefore, we appreciate the opportunity to witness the shared love of this beautiful couple. Their enthusiasm is contagious, their certainty of their destiny together is inspiring and their great expectations give us all a glimpse of the heights love can reach.

Marriage is a very special place. It's an oasis, a haven, and a sanctuary where we can safely learn about ourselves in the presence of another. Like the harmony with the melody, marriage weaves two lives together, creating a deeper and richer song. We are honored that _____ and _____ are sharing some of **their** beautiful music with us on this day.

We ask that the vision they have of one another always reflect the electric attraction that first brought them together. And we pray that, as they enter into the lifelong bond that is marriage, they may always see one another in the light of all light; the light of love.

Gathering Words #5

We have come together, families and friends, to witness _____ and _____ as they exchange their vows of marriage. We share with them their delight in finding love with each other, and support their decision to be together from now until the end of time.

As this couple enters into marriage, they do so with thought and reverence. They give thanks for the past, which brought them to this place, and look forward with hope to what the future will bring.

Marriage is like a great umbrella that shelters love from the elements. Corinthians One says that love is patient and kind. It is not jealous or boastful, not irritable or resentful, not arrogant or rude. Love does not insist on its own way. It does not rejoice in the wrong, but rejoices in the right. Love bears all things, believes all things, hopes in all things and endures all things. Love never ends. This marriage is a symbol of _____ & _____'s commitment to that love.

A Few Comments About The Prayers

The prayers/blessings here are pretty simple. It's a way of including God, the Supreme Being, Higher Power, whatever, and asking for the big 'thumbs up'. It's also a way of recognizing your very important role in the scheme of things and sets the mood for the rest of the ceremony.

It's just a nice way to send out a little hello to someone whose help you might like later on in life.

As with any of the parts, take what you like and leave the rest.

Opening Prayer #1

Let us pray. God, we ask for your blessings upon this man and woman (couple), as we celebrate this momentous occasion in their lives.

Grant them happiness and contentment as they establish their new home, create a new family and explore the depths of their love for one another and for you.

Bless their families and friends and the relationships, which have supported, strengthened and sustained them throughout their lives.

Bless their home as a place of love and of peace.

And if times grow hard and tempers grow short, help them to look into their hearts and remember the love that brought them here today.

Amen

Opening Prayer #2

God, as you join us today, we ask for your blessings upon this couple as they unite in marriage.

Let all their days together be happy and all their words to each other be sweet.

Though their paths are intertwined, let them be aware of each other's separateness. Bless their home and allow it to be a place of joy and serenity.

Remind them to nurture each other's body with mutual love, honor and respect. Let their spirits dwell within.

As they learn from one another, may they grow stronger as individuals and closer as a couple.

And as their wedded life begins today with prayer, so may they continue it, praying for and with each other.

Amen.

How To Gain Some
Support From Families

This next part is a way to include family members in the ceremony. Often, this part is for the fathers of the couple. There was a time, in days gone past, where a woman was considered property of her father and therefore could be 'given away' in marriage. Such is not the case anymore, but the tradition continues.

In this more modern rendering, the parents of both the bride and groom may stand to offer their love and support of the happy couple. After the bride has joined her groom at the altar, the person who walked her down (usually the father) gets a kiss on the cheek, shakes hands with the groom, then sits down.

Then, a little way into the ceremony, the fathers say something like, "Her mother and I do" at the appropriate time. But this is not always the case. With families changing such as they are, it may be that the mom says it, step-parents, both sets of parents, etc. The important thing is that it's someone who loves and supports you as a couple. It can even be your kids.

You might not think your parent will want to say anything during the ceremony, but you'd be surprised how many are flattered to be asked -- especially the family of the groom. They often get a bit left out, since most of the focus is on the bride and her family.

Support From Families #1

The marriage of _____ & _____ brings together two different families; two unique story lines, so a new chapter in their lives can begin to unfold.

Though this relationship was formed out of the love these two have found in each other, their marriage will ultimately be blessed by the support of their families.

Who stands with this woman to symbolize her family's support of this union?

"I do"-----"We do"---or ---"Her mother and I do"

Who stands with this man to symbolize his family's support of this union?

"I do"----"We do"---or---"His mother and I do"

Support From Families (And Friends) #2

The marriage of _____ & _____ is more than just the union of two people in love. It's also the joining of two families, of two sets of friends and of two patterns of life.

Who stands with this woman in support and blessing of this marriage?

"I do" or "Her Mother and I do"

Who stands with this man in support and blessing of this marriage?

"I do" or "His Mother and I do"

As these two people join together in marriage, they ask for the support and love of not only their families, but of their friends as well.

On this day, they ask that you be more than only friends of _____ or only friends of _____. They ask that you recognize their special union and welcome them both as your friends in your lives.

The Inside Poop About The 'Charge To Couple' and 'Consent' Sections

The 'charge to couple' is one of those 'really pretty words' sections I was telling you about. It's a word or two directed to the couple that talks about what it means to be married and some hints about how to be successful at it. It's also a reminder to the bride and groom that the covenant of marriage is not to be entered into lightly and helps them to recognize the seriousness of their decision.

The 'consent' section has a little history though. It was originally used for shotgun weddings. If a boy got a gal pregnant, the father of said gal would point a shotgun at the young man, asking him ever so politely if he was 'free to be married'.

This is also a way of confirming that neither party is currently married or has any other problems prohibiting the union from taking place. However, this is not the same as the 'promise'. That comes later.

Charge To Couple #1

_____ & _____, as you stand here in the presence of God and these witnesses, I remind you, that love, loyalty and trust are the basis of a mature and fulfilling relationship.

Marriage is a serious undertaking; it is intended to bind your lives together forever and is not to be taken lightly. Your engagement set into motion the interweaving of your lives - and we hope that you will continue to grow closer throughout your years together.

None of us knows what the future will bring. Yet your love for one another, and trust in the strength of your union makes possible the act of faith you are making today.

As you exchange the vows, which will start you on your journey together, know that our love and support go with you. As you make your promises to each other, we will remember promises we too have made and take this opportunity to make new our own.

Charge To Couple #2

This is a new beginning for both of you and I'd like to offer some gentle reminders to ease your life-long task of living and growing together.

Be kind to each other. And, when you disagree, do it respectfully.

Be gentle and forgiving with each other. When you forgive, your hearts make room for a little more love, a little more understanding and a little more compassion.

Communicate with each other. Share the joy that's in your heart and the sorrow that burdens your soul. Open your hearts to each other and find the love.

Charge To Couple #3

_____ and _____, as you stand here today, I remind you of the serious nature of the relationship you are about to enter. Marriage is the voluntary and full commitment of two consenting adults to love each other for a lifetime.

For a marriage to be successful, you must each be loyal to the other, stand firm in your defense of each other and be supportive of one another's life goals and dreams. It is a solemn, binding, yet challenging relationship.

Consent #1

_____, do you come here today, in the presence of these witnesses, with love in your heart and with a conscious desire to be united in marriage with _____? Do you promise to share the responsibility for growth and enrichment of your lives together and to give to _____ all the loving support she needs to become the person she is destined to be?

"I do"

_____, do you come here today, in the presence of these witnesses, with love in your heart and with a conscious desire to be united in marriage with _____? Do you promise to share the responsibility for growth and enrichment of your lives together and to give to _____ all the loving support he needs to become the person he is destined to be?

"I do"

Consent #2

_____, do you here in the presence of family and friends, declare your love for and commitment to _____, choosing her as your life partner and soul mate? Do you freely offer yourself to her and willingly accept the gift of self she offers to you?

"I do"

_____, do you here in the presence of family and friends, declare your love for and commitment to _____, choosing him as your life partner and soul mate? Do you freely offer yourself to him and willingly accept the gift of self he offers to you?

"I do"

How *NOT* To Get Burned By The Candle-lighting Ceremony

This is probably the most common ritual done at weddings (aside from the exchanging of rings). It's done with at least two skinny candles and one thicker candle, also called a 'unity' candle. It is aptly named because it symbolizes the unity of the couple.

This can be done a few different ways. The simplest way is to have the minister light the two tapered candles before the ceremony. When the ceremony calls for it, the minister moves aside, the couple steps up and each takes a tapered candle, lighting the center one together.

Another way is to have the mothers of the bride and groom walk down the aisle during the processional, up to the altar, and each light a tapered candle then. Another suggestion is to have the mothers of the bride and groom each hold a tapered candle during the beginning of the ceremony. When the time is right, they can light their candles, stand, give them to their children respectively, then sit down. The couple then proceeds to the unity candle and lights it. The last ceremony mentioned envelops the concept of passing the torch, sharing a spark of themselves, etc.

The large, ornate unity candles tend to be pretty expensive, so if you're on a tight budget, you can decorate a candle yourself or just buy one in your wedding colors. A scented candle is a nice touch as well.

Candle-lighting Ceremony #1

_____ & _____, together as you light this candle of unity, you symbolize the flame of your own individual selves joining to ignite the partnership of marriage.

You also bring the warmth, strength and wisdom of your family's fire as kindling for your own.

As _____ & _____, your flames are separate, yet they feed the same fire.

From this day onward, may you bask in the beauty of the light of your love, may its light shine bright and steady upon your path together and may its heat keep you warm through all the days of your lives and beyond.

Candle-lighting Ceremony #2

This candle you are about to light is a candle of Marriage. Its fire is magical because it represents the light of two people in love.

This candle before you is a candle of Commitment because it takes two people working together to keep it aflame.

This candle is also a candle of Unity because both must come together, a spark of themselves, to create the new light.

As you light this candle today, may the brightness of the flame shine throughout your lives. May it give you courage and reassurance in darkness; warmth and safety in the cold; and strength and joy in your bodies, minds, and spirits.

May your union be forever blessed.

Getting Giddy About A Wine Ceremony

The wine ceremony is a fairly common ritual done at weddings. The concept is similar to that of the candle-lighting ceremony. It symbolizes the two people coming together as they form their marriage bond.

The wine ceremony can be done two ways. The first is to have one wine glass filled with a liquid. (I'd suggest a clear liquid in case any spills happen.) After the minister talks about the meaning, the glass is handed to the groom, who takes a sip; he hands it to his bride, who takes a sip and the bride hands it back to the minister. Piece of cake. (Actually, that comes later.)

The other way encompasses the idea about drinking together but not from one glass, eating together, but not of the same loaf, etc. This ceremony can be done using two glasses and intertwining arms as you both take a sip. It's cute and very romantic.

<u>Wine Ceremony #1</u>

Life is a series of contradictions. It is said that all things end and yet all things continue. All things change and yet all things remain the same.

Wine has been called the symbol of life. It's like the blood flowing within our bodies. By sharing this glass, the two become one, the parts become whole, two paths intertwined, each separate, yet united in love.

Wine Ceremony #2

Wine, like the life-blood that pulses through our veins, is a symbol of life. It is created through the work of hands and minds.

Love, a feeling, in constant motion like the sea, lies in the soul alone. Just as wine stimulates the body, love stimulates our souls to welcome the spirit of God.

As you share this wine glass today, may you be joined in a love as fluid as the drink itself, yet as solid as the hands which made it.

Wine Ceremony #3

This wineglass is to remind you of your love. Delicate, yet strong; filled with love, yet with room for more. It symbolizes two people coming together to share one life, one love.

Use this loving cup for miracles. Fill it with forgiveness, understanding and appreciation. Drink deeply and often. Whenever you do, remember this:

Love is real. Once created, it cannot be destroyed. It is eternal.

Wine Ceremony #4

This glass of wine symbolizes the sum of your life experiences. It contains within it the sweet flavors of love, joy, wonder and contentment.

This same cup, at times, holds the bitter taste of sadness, pain, and despair. When you drink deeply of this cup of life, you invite the full spectrum of experiences into your life.

As you drink from this cup, you accept the commitment to draw from your marriage all that you need to wash away the bitter flavors of life and to savor the sweet flavors you may encounter on your journey together.

The Vows That Bind

The vows are probably the most intimate part of the whole ceremony. This is the part where you get to try and put into words the intense feelings you have for your beloved. This is no easy task. There are quite a few to choose from here. You can pick one that suits you, or use these as a guide to write your own.

Most people, when they get to the vows during the ceremony, prefer to have the minister say them slowly, calmly, line by line, and have you repeat them. I personally think this is a good idea.

Or, if you're brave, you can memorize the whole thing and try to remember it when you're up there, really nervous, in front of all of your friends and family, taking the biggest step of your life. It is, of course, up to you, but be sure to give the minister a copy of your vows in case you need prompting.

It also may be a good idea to keep some smelling salts on hand; you know, just in case. Refer to the *Emergency Kit For Wedding Day*.

Vows #1

(Take _____ by the hand and say to her:)

_____, I take you to be my wife;

To share with you the laughter;
To kiss away the tears;
And to give you all the love in my heart,
As long as we both shall live.

_____, I take you to be my husband;

To share with you the laughter;
To kiss away the tears;
And to give you all the love in my heart,
As long as we both shall live.

Vows #2

Please repeat after me:

I _____, take you _____ to be my wife:

To love you when you drive me crazy.
To respect you when we disagree.
To support you if bad times come our way.
And to always remember how grateful I am
To have you by my side.

I _____, take you _____ to be my husband:

To love you when you drive me crazy.
To respect you when we disagree.
To support you if bad times come our way.
And to always remember how grateful I am
To have you by my side.

Vows #3

Please turn to your bride please and repeat after me:

_____, I take you to be my wife:

To love you with all my heart;
To share with you all my soul;
To grow with you through all my days;
As long as we both shall live.

_____, I take you to be my husband:

To love you with all my heart;
To share with you all my soul;
To grow with you through all my days;
As long as we both shall live.

Vows #4

(Please turn to your bride and repeat after me.)

From this day onward, I choose you _____ to be my wife.

To live together and laugh together;
To work by your side and dream in your arms;
To fill your heart and feed your soul;
To always seek out the best in you;
To play with you whenever I can, as we grow old;
Always loving you with all my heart, until the end of our forever.

(Please repeat after me.)

From this day onward, I choose you _____ to be my husband.

To live together and laugh together;
To work by your side and dream in your arms;
To fill your heart and feed your soul;
To always seek out the best in you;
To play with you whenever I can, as we grow old;
Always loving you with all my heart, until the end of our forever.

Vows #5

_____, turn to your bride please and repeat after me:

I choose you _____ to be my wife. (companion)
I have emptied my heart of all others.
It is only filled with you.
You're my best friend and my only love
And I'll cherish you for the rest of my life.

_____, please repeat after me:

I choose you, _____ to be my husband. (companion)
I have emptied my heart of all others.
It is only filled with you.
You're my best friend and my only love
And I'll cherish you for the rest of my life.

Vows #6

(Inspired by Dr. Seuss's Green Eggs and Ham)

Groom: I will love you on the sea
I will love you in a tree
I will love you here and there
I will love you anywhere.

Bride: I will love you everyday
I will love you come what may
I will love you more than pie
I will love you 'til I die

Groom: On the sea, in a tree.

Bride: Every day, come what may.

Together: I will love you here and there.
I will love you anywhere.

Traditional Promises/Rings/Vows

(These can be used as promises rings or vows; edit as needed.)

As you place the ring on _____'s finger, answer me this (*or repeat after me*):

Do you _____ take _____ to be your lawfully wedded (wife/husband)? From this day forward, to have and to hold, for better, for worse, for richer and for poorer, in sickness and in health, to love and to cherish, 'til death do you part?'

"I do"

Guest Participation of Vows

And now, _____ & _____ have a wedding gift to give all of you gathered here today. As they speak their vows to one another, they'd like to give you the chance to experience the same affirmation of love. Because love is alive, it blossoms when shared with others.

They ask you to think of anyone to whom you'd like to say, "I love you." Whether a spouse, sibling, child, parent or friend. Close your eyes and see the place within. Create a picture of that person in your minds' eye and speak to that picture. Grasp that person's hand as _____ & _____ each grasp theirs and silently repeat after me:

(Bride & Groom repeat out loud to each other simultaneously)

I love you and respect you.
I appreciate the gift of your love.
Knowing you has enriched my life beyond measure.
You make my life complete.

Now say good-bye to that person and wish them well, while we celebrate with _____ & _____ and bless their good fortune.

Promise Of A Lifetime

The promise section is the part where, traditionally, you would promise to love, honor, and (choke) obey. Most people replace that last part with 'cherish' or 'respect.' This is the part where, after you've stated you terms in the vows, you agree to be married. The traditional one talk, about having, holding, richer, poorer, etc. The ones offered here sa that as well, in a variety of ways.

There is also a part for families. When a couple gets married, and t ere are children involved, it's a nice gesture of unity to invite them to nake promises as well.

If the new stepparent already has a strong bond with the child, then it's a statement of love and affection. If their bonds are still forming, it's a great way to open your heart and theirs and (hopefully) increase the lines of communication. Something to think about. This is also an appropriate place to give the children gifts of medallions or rings as a symbol of family unity.

If you'd like to do something a little different, you can do the 'Affirmation of the Community'. This gives all your guests an opportunity to say they will stand by you as a couple.

Be sure the minister is comfortable with this and knows to prompt the guests beforehand or you may find an embarrassing silence when this part comes up.

Promises #1

_____ & _____, by coming here today, you have reached a crossroads in your lives. You're turning away from your yesterdays and looking ahead to your tomorrows. Your past is a distant memory. Your future a waiting adventure. It is a new dawn, a new commitment, a new life. The bonds you are forging today will change your lives forever.

Do you, _____, promise to take _____ to be your (wife/husband)? To play with (her/him) and care for (her/him); to make (her/him) laugh, and let (her/him) cry? To offer your best counsel and give your sincerest support with all the love you have to give?

"I do."

Is it your choice that _____ be the one with whom you wish to spend your life?

"It is."

Promises #2

Do you _____ promise to love _____ and respect (him/her), to share your life and your dreams, to build with (him/her) a home that is a place of love, happiness, commitment and growth?

"I do"

Do you promise to be a companion to (her/him) in all of (her/him) successes and failures, (her/his) happiness and sadness, to always give to (her/him) your unwavering support and above all else, the freedom to be _____ (name)?

"I do"

Promises #3

_____, do you take _____ to be the wife of your days, the companion of your heart and the friend of your life? To stand united in the face of adversity and bask together in the light of good fortune? With these words spoken, and all those as yet unspoken, do you wish to marry _____ and join your life with hers?

"I do."

_____, do you take _____ to be the husband of your days, the companion of your heart and the friend of your life? To stand united in the face of adversity and bask together in the light of good fortune? With these words spoken, and all those as yet unspoken, do you wish to marry _____ and join your life with his?

"I do."

Promises #4

Do you _____ promise to love _____ freely – without restrictions; honestly – without deceit; now – without hesitation?

"I do."

Do you promise to accept (her/him) just as (she/he) is, sharing with (her/him) and supporting (her/him) through the experiences of your lives, be they easy or difficult, happy or sad, challenging or mundane, till death do you part?

"I do."

Family Promises

Because of the vows they have taken today, _____ & _____ have created a whole new family. To make their commitment to that new family complete, they wish to include their children: _____ and recognize them as an integral part of this marriage. (giving them each a medallion to symbolize their new family unity.)

Do you _____ take (children of spouse) to be the (son/daughter) children of your heart, to love and to hug, to talk to and to learn from, through successes and growing pains, as long as you all shall live?

"I do."

Do you (children) take _____ to be your step- (mom/dad) and your friend, accomplice and ally, to love and to hug (cherish), as long as you all shall live?

"I (we) do."

(Do you, Bride's children & Groom's children, each take the other(s) to be your (sister/brother) and your friend(s), through fights and through fun, as long as you all shall live?)

"We do."

Do you, (Parent), promise to support these relationships, to give them room to breathe, to encourage their special bonds with each other and love them through it all?

"I do"

Family Unity Candle

This candle you are about to light is a candle of Family. Its fire is magical because it burns with the flame of a family joined in love.

This candle before you is a candle of Commitment because it takes (three, four, *etc.*) people working together to keep it aflame.

This candle is also a candle of Unity because *all* must come together, giving a spark of themselves, to create the new light.

As you light this candle today, may the brightness of the flame shine throughout your lives. May it give you courage and reassurance in darkness; warmth and safety in the cold; and strength and joy in your bodies, minds, and spirits.

May your family be forever blessed.

Affirmation Of The Community

The union of _____ & _____ has joined us together because we are each reflected in it. A new family has been created in our community, and we have come here today to welcome them and celebrate their new relationship.

Do you, who are the family and friends of this couple, affirm your continuing support of and love for _____ & _____ as they stand poised on the threshold of their new life together?

"We do."

Ring A Ding Ding

The whole ring event is something that causes some people considerable stress. Who carries the ring? When do we get the rings? How do I get it out from around my collar, etc.? I'll try to help clear up any confusion you may have.

Okay, first of all, you may decide to have a ring bearer. If the ring bearer is younger than five years old or very nervous about the whole thing, you may decide to put fake rings on the pillow or no rings at all. Then there's no stress about whether or not he'll make it down the aisle and what he might do when he gets there. I saw one ring bearer pass out during the ceremony. It was hot out and he was nervous, so he just collapsed. Fortunately, he was fine and the rings had already been retrieved, but still it was disruptive.

If you do entrust your rings to the ring bearer, he can do two things with them. He can (1) keep them attached to the ring pillow until that part comes up in the ceremony, then let the bride and groom remove them. Or (2) he can walk down the aisle to the maid of honor and have her take the groom's ring, step over to the best man and have him take the bride's ring, then sit down or stand with the men.

A third possibility is not to have a ring bearer and have the maid of honor and best man each hold a ring. All of those ways will work. Again, it's up to you how you want to work it.

A hint about the ring ceremony itself; you may want to put a little lotion on your ring finger so the ring slides on more easily.

Rings #1

The ring is an ancient symbol, so perfect and simple. It has no beginning and has no end. It is round like the sun, like the moon, like the eye, like arms that embrace. It is a circle; for love that is given comes back round again.

Your rings are precious because you wear them with love. They symbolize your commitment in marriage. They remind you of who you are, where you've been, and where you're going. As you wear them through time, they will reflect not only who you are as individuals, but also who you are as a couple.

As you place the ring on _____'s finger, please repeat after me:

You are the love of my life
And you are my very best friend

May these rings remind you that your love, like the sun, warms all that it touches, like the moon, brightens up the night, like the eye, is a gateway to your innermost soul. And your love, like the arms that embrace you, makes everything right with the world.

Rings #2

These rings are made of precious metals; purified by the heat of many fires. They are a symbol of the wealth that resides inside each of you and the purity of your love for one another.

As you place the ring on (her/his) finger, please repeat after me:

I give you this ring to wear
As a symbol of my abiding love,
My eternal faith, and my undying devotion.
It is an outward reminder of our inner unity.

Rings #3

Though we have heard the vows, which have been shared by _____ & _____, words, once spoken, are carried away on the wind. Therefore, the wedding ring is a visible symbol of the promises that have been made.

As you place the ring on (his/her) finger, please repeat after me:

With this ring, I marry you and bind my life to yours.
It is a symbol of my eternal love,
My everlasting friendship,
And the promise of all my tomorrows.

May these wedding rings be a reminder to _____ & _____ of the commitment they have made today and be a testimony to all the world of their devotion in marriage.

<u>Rings #4</u>

The circle has frequently been used to symbolize eternity.

The ring, like the circle, is a reminder of the perfection and endurance of _____ and _____'s commitment to and love for one another.

As you place the ring on (her/his) finger, please repeat after me:

This ring I give you
Is a symbol of my love.
I pledge to share with you my heart,
My home, and all (most?) of my worldly goods.

<u>Rings #5</u>

These rings represent the vows and promises you've willingly exchanged. They reflect the commitment those words inspire and all your hopes and dreams for the future.

As you place the ring on (his/her) finger, please repeat after me:

With this ring, I marry you:
With my loving heart.
With my willing body.
And with my eternal soul.

May the vows and promises you have made today be as ever-present in your hearts as these rings are on your fingers.

Rings #6

Marriage is a state in which two people come together and create a union that is greater than the sum of its parts. It is difficult to express in words the profound relationship that is love.

Since the beginning of time, the ring has been an emblem of the sincerity and permanence of a couple's love for one another and regard for their marriage.

As the circle can begin anew at any point, so a good marriage can pick any point to renew itself. These rings are symbols of your eternal love.

As you place the ring on (her/his) finger, please repeat after me:

I give you this ring as a reminder that I will love, honor, and cherish you,
In all times,
In all places,
And in all ways, forever.

Ending On A High Note With A Blessing & Benediction

The difference between a blessing and a benediction is that the former talks more to God about the happy couple and the benediction talks more to the happy couple about themselves. You can have both, either or neither.

What it comes down to is whether or not you like what's said. Do the words speak to you and what you want to convey? This is what's important.

During most church services, the benediction comes at the very end of everything, right before you go out for refreshments. In the case of weddings, I found that after I pronounced the couple married, the benediction got lost in the applause. It was rather anti-climactic. That's why I suggest putting it just before the wedding pronouncement.

If there is more than one benediction that you like, there's room in the ceremony for one to be put between the wine ceremony and the candle-lighting, if you're not having a reading or a song. Bear in mind that even if you had one of everything, including the dove release, the ceremony probably won't exceed 25 min. Maybe a half-hour if you have a singer performing a song. It goes really fast when you're up there.

<u>Blessing #1</u>

May your lives be filled with wisdom, blessed with good health, and abundant with miracles.

May you eternally have your amusement, remembering how to play, and may you always see the connection that brought you both together.

Blessing #2

_____ & _____, we are here today to celebrate with you, as you declare your love for and commitment to each other. We are also here to offer you the gift of our blessings.

We wish for you love – a love that brings out the best in you, as you bring out the best in each other. One that gives you something to lean on when you need it most. And one that allows you to see each other as you really are, reminding you why you're together.

We wish for you a home – more just a place to live, but a haven from the pressures of the world outside your door. A place to let down your guard, unburden yourself and know that there's someone always on your side.

Finally, we wish for you joy – a joy that makes you laugh out loud. A joy that lights your eyes and fills your soul. And a joy that shouts to the world of your happiness with one another.

All this and more we wish for you today, and every day throughout the years of your marriage.

<u>Blessing #3</u>

May you be blessed and sustained as you venture through the uncharted and challenging times that every relationship experiences.

May you find within yourselves all that you need to nurture your marriage.

May you continue to grow closer together with a love that grows deeper and richer with each passing day.

Benediction #1

Remember that your love is the basis for this marriage; desire nothing else, fear nothing else and allow your love to blossom into what love was meant to be.

Allow for spaces in your time together, giving each other room to grow. Love one another; allow that love to be a source of strength, which feeds your soul.

None of us knows what the future will bring . . . the important thing is to live today to the fullest and face tomorrow with the certainty that you can accept and handle what it brings.

Benediction #2

May your love be one based on freedom. For though our hands may touch, it's our hearts that hold.

When you hold love within your heart, you radiate a light, which shall brighten all the days of your life and beyond.

Everything we truly love, becomes a part of us forever. So take your time with each other. Let your love's seed grow and mature with the seasons, to provide you with warmth, serenity, joy and acceptance throughout all the years of your marriage.

Love is not a wall; it is a bridge. Love does not confine; it sets you free. It leads, as a pathway, winding, to places unknown and mysterious. With love to light the way, you can meet any challenge, together.

Benediction #3

Go into the world and fulfill your dreams. Love, support, and help one another as you grow. Seek out opportunities to be good to each other.

May the seeds of your love, now planted in marriage, continue to grow. May your life together be as a pebble dropped in a pond; an example of love and unity spread outward to your family, your friends and to the wider circle of the world.

Benediction #4

_____ & _____, you came here today, in the presence of family and friends, to express your love for, and commitment to each other. Your lives are forever changed.

Now, you can face your fears, for you each will be strength to the other.

Now, you can brave the wind, for you each will be shelter to the other.

Now, you can reap the rewards, for you each will be partner to the other.

Now though you are two bodies, there is one life before you.

And there, in that life, may you always find love.

Benediction #5

May you be blessed by God. May you be touched by angels.

May your hearts stay full, your spirits stay connected, and may you love long and happily in one another's arms.

Benediction #6

Today, you are embarking on a new journey. This is a journey no two have traveled before; it is unique to you.

It is up to you to make the most of your life together. Dream big dreams, love like there's no tomorrow and become the best people you know how to be.

'Tying It Up' With The Ribbon Ceremony &
'Letting It Go' With The Dove/Butterfly Release

The ribbon ceremony is a nice way to involve children into the service. What you do is stand side by side either facing each other or facing the minister. Hold hands. During this part, your children approach on cue and lightly tie a ribbon around your wrists, tying you together and blessing your union. You can play music during this time or not. It doesn't take very long unless there are a lot of children involved. Use your best judgment.

The dove or butterfly release can be done before or after the marriage pronouncement. I would suggest doing it immediately before. Some people do a balloon release, but since the balloons end up killing a lot of birds (they swallow the plastic), it's sort of frowned upon. Doves and butterflies are beautiful and add a dramatic flair to the event. In some places though, pigeons are substituted for doves because the doves don't survive well in certain climates. (Pigeons still look really good though.)

The butterflies are sold by the dozen, usually and are put in small, triangular boxes just prior to the wedding. They seem to hibernate and immediately take to flight upon release. If you're nervous about them dying before you get to release them, you may want to keep two extra on the table at the altar, just in case. You can also order them individually in little habitats.

One very important thing about doing a release: Do Not Do It Inside! Well, okay, you probably figured that, but I thought best to mention it just to be safe.

Ribbon Ceremony
(For those who want to include children.)

On this day, _____ & _____ came together as man and woman to be joined in marriage. It is, however, more than just the union of two people in love. It is also the joining of two families.

We ask today for the blessings of the children (or fill in child's name here). We ask that each child of _____ and _____ approach the couple and show his or her support of the couple by blessing their union with a ribbon of love.

Music Plays

(Each of the couples' children approach couple and loosely bind their wrists together with ribbon.)

Dove Release #1

Doves are beautiful, devoted creatures. Watching them soar together in synchronous flight is an inspiration and a joy to watch.

They symbolize unity, loyalty, love, beauty, devotion and peace – all that you wish for yourselves throughout your own life together.

As you release them into flight, send with them your own hopes and dreams, which will soar with the birds, to soon come back to you.

(Possible song cue here.)

Dove Release #2

Doves have been used for centuries to symbolize all the hope, peace and love that come from new beginnings. As they release this pair into flight, we who are here today, join them in wishing that all that is good will go with them into their new life together.

Watch closely as the birds fly. Together they will create beautiful patterns in the sky; sometimes apart, sometimes together, always in harmony with one another. This is how it is with a good marriage. Two people moving together, both on their own paths, yet united in their journey.

As you begin your adventure today, we wish for you to enjoy the beauty of your flight, the intricacies of the patterns you create, and the peace such a journey can bring.

<u>Butterfly Release</u>

Butterflies are as beautiful as they are fragile. They symbolize transformation and all that is perfect in the world. As you two join today in marriage, your commitment to love releases into the world a new wonder, a new beauty, a new perfection.

One of the secrets of being happy with one you love, is to take hold lightly and let go lightly. As you release these gentle creatures, may your love transform itself and everyone it touches into its highest form.

About The Author

Rev. Amy Long has been a non-denominational minister since 1991. She has been involved in hundreds of weddings, as a minister, vocalist, disc jockey and once, as a bride. She is a resident of Elk Grove, CA, where she lives with her husband and children. She also owns and operates the company called *A Budget Jockey DJ*.

If you are interested in having her perform your wedding, she can be reached at (916) 535-7685, by e-mail at Spiritual1@aol.com or at her website www.weddingwordsandmore.com.